Level F

Stepping Into Reading

A Guided Approach to Critical Thinking

Vickey Herold

MODERN CURRICULUM PRESS
CLEVELAND ■ TORONTO

To the Student

Stepping into Reading teaches skills that you can use to become a better thinker, a better reader and a better writer. In each lesson there is a short story, followed by exercises. These exercises will show you how to get the most out of your reading experience. Many of the exercises require creative thought, and often there are no "right" or "wrong" answers. It is up to you to provide the best solutions.

The skills you learn can be applied to everything you read. They will help you think effectively throughout your life.

To the Teacher

Stepping into Reading is a workbook series that teaches strategies for promoting growth in inferential and creative thinking. High-interest reading selections are the basis of the program. Lessons need not be taught in order of presentation; however, within any given lesson, the sections should be followed exactly. For your convenience, the sections are the same: prior knowledge, guided reading, story mapping, vocabulary development and writing. Each section is designed to establish and cultivate critical thinking skills in students. Hence, there are often no right or wrong answers. Answers are included when applicable, in a key at the back of the book.

Acknowledgments
Project Directors: Linda R. Post, Deborah Russell Ray
Project design and art: M.D.C. Publishing Services
Photo Research and Credits: M.D.C. Publishing Services

Modern Curriculum Press, Inc.
A Division of Simon & Schuster
13900 Prospect Road
Cleveland, Ohio 44136

Published simultaneously in Canada by Globe / Modern Curriculum Press, Toronto.

ISBN 0-8136-1668-9 (F) 3 4 5 6 7 8 9 10 95 94 93 92

Table of Contents

Lesson 1: INCIDENT AT DICKENS CREEK

by Vickey Herold

GET INTO STEP Prior Knowledge

1. Think about each of the following questions. Answer at least one question on the lines below.

- Were you ever worried about telling your friends something because you knew it would make them angry at you? What happened?
- Were you ever friends with someone you didn't like at first? Tell about it.
- Think about a time when you were really excited about going somewhere. Where was it? How did you feel?

____

____

____

____

2. What do you think "Incident at Dickens Creek" will be about? Write some predictions.

____

____

____

____

STEP INTO THE STORY Guided Reading

Read "Incident at Dickens Creek" to see if any of your predictions are true. As you read the story, you will come to several breaking points. You will be asked to think, to react and to write.

About a month ago my Aunt Dottie came to visit. Aunt Dottie's okay, but I can't say the same for her son, my cousin, Ned. Ned had always been a real pain in the neck! The two of us just never had anything in common. When Mom told us at the dinner table one night that Ned and Aunt Dottie were coming to stay for a week, I really flipped out!

Were you ever upset about someone who was coming for a visit? ____________

If so, do you think that the boy in the story feels the same way? ____________

"Now, Donnie," Mom warned, "you'd better behave yourself. I think that your Aunt Dottie is sweet to give up a whole week to help me take inventory at the store. I'd never make it without her. You know that it's too much for me to handle myself."

"Yes'um," I answered sheepishly.

"And it won't hurt you to be nice to Ned, either. I want you to invite him to go on the camp-out that you're planning with your friends."

"Oh, Mom!" I pleaded. "You can't be serious. Ned the Nerd on our camp-out—the guys will hate me!"

"Donnie," she said very sternly with one eyebrow raised high, "either Ned goes or you don't. Is that clear?"

"Yes'um, I guess so."

I was sick! Ned the Nerd on the camp-out we'd been planning for weeks. How was I going to tell the guys? I just couldn't. So I decided not to say anything. I decided that I'd just show up with Ned. Then it would be too late for the guys to do anything about it.

Do you agree with Donnie's decision not to tell his friends about Ned? ________

What would you have done? ____

____

The next Friday evening, Aunt Dottie and Ned arrived just before dinner. I was upstairs when they came in, but I didn't have to be told that Ned was in the house. I could hear him sniffing and snorting all the way up the stairs.

"Hi, Donnie," he wheezed as he shoved a bottle of nasal spray up his nose and squeezed it hard. "How ya been?"

"O.K." I answered flatly, without looking up from the book I was reading. I thought maybe he'd figure out that I really didn't have anything to say to him—but he didn't. I guess he was used to being ignored. He just kept on talking.

"Your mom tells me that we're going on some kind of a camping trip tomorrow."

"Yeah," I answered with my eyes still on the book.

"So, where are we going, anyhow?" I didn't answer. He raised his voice. "I said where are we going?" He stuffed the nasal spray up his other nostril.

"Dickens Creek," I said and shot him a dirty look.

"Oh. Well, I hope you're not planning on sleeping outside or anything dumb like that," he wheezed and blew his nose. "Sorry . . . allergies, you know."

"Yeah, I know," I said. "And, yes, we're sleeping outside, and if you don't like it, you can stay here!"

"Well, I guess if you guys want to sleep out, I can too," Ned mumbled as he pushed his thick glasses back up on his nose.

How do you think Donnie feels about his cousin, Ned? Write some words that describe what Donnie is feeling. ______________________________

____

My friends Alex and Carlos were at our house by nine the next morning. I met them at the door and was about to break the news about Ned when he came stumbling down the hall. He was wearing enough coats and sweaters for three people and carrying a large briefcase in one hand and a suitcase in the other. On his head was a red and black checked hat with ear flaps that made his glasses hang crooked across his silly face.

Why is Ned carrying a briefcase and a suitcase on a camping trip? Make some predictions about what might be inside. ______________________

____

____

"Hi, guys," Ned wheezed. "It's a pleasure to be included for your little weekend. I'm sure it'll be a real learning opportunity, you know . . . the call of the wild . . . man against nature . . . intellect against the elements."

Alex and Carlos stood there with their mouths hanging open. Then they turned to me to explain what they couldn't believe they were seeing.

"Carlos, Alex . . . this is my cousin, Ned. He's going along." I knew that my only chance was to talk fast and get moving before they could object.

What do you suppose Alex and Carlos think about Ned? ______________________

____

Explain your answer. ______________________

____

The rest of the day was like a nightmare. Ned followed us around talking about all kinds of dumb, boring stuff. He coughed and wheezed and scared the fish away with his sneezing attacks. He complained about the cold and the dampness and the wind and the smoke from the fire. He pushed on his glasses and rubbed in his creams and swallowed his pills every time his alarm watch sounded. It seemed that whenever I looked his way he had his nasal spray shoved up his nose. He was, in short, a real joy to have around!

How would *you* feel about being on a camp-out with Ned? Explain your answer. ______________________________

____

____

When we decided to turn in, I knew better than to ask about the sleeping arrangements. I knew that I was doomed to share a tent with Ned. I crawled inside and pulled the blanket up over my head and tried to go to sleep as quickly as possible. I guess I was pretty tired, because even Ned's snorting didn't keep me from going to sleep almost immediately.

It must have been several hours later when shouting woke me up suddenly. I heard Carlos and Alex yelling and the sound of twigs breaking and leaves crackling as if someone were running through the woods. I struggled to wake up and look outside the tent, but I was tangled in the blankets. When I finally managed to struggle free, I turned to crawl out of the front of the small tent—but stopped instantly. The black eyes of a huge bear met mine. Very slowly I backed back inside.

"Ned," I whispered coarsely. He didn't move. The nerd was sleeping like a baby! I reached out cautiously and shook his shoulder. "Ned, wake up!"

"I'm coming, Mom," he mumbled. "Just five more minutes and I'll get up."

"Ned, you dope," I whispered more panicked than before. "Wake up, we're about to be attacked by a bear!"

"Pear?" Ned asked, still more asleep than awake. "Sure, a pear for breakfast would be nice, Mom."

"Not PEAR, you nerd! BEAR!" This time I was shouting.

Ned was awake now. He fumbled around for his glasses all the while mumbling, "Bear? Bear what? What are you talking about?"

Ned crawled toward the front of the tent feeling around the ground for his glasses. Just as he found them and put them on, the bear stuck his head inside the tent to see what all the commotion was about. He and Ned were practically nose to nose.

"Yipe!" Ned screamed. "There's a bear in here!" His hand came down on his bottle of nasal spray and in one quick motion he picked it up, aimed it right in the bear's face and squeezed for all he was worth! The unsuspecting bear got a huge squirt of nasal spray in his eyes and nose and raised up with a big bellow! He took off into the woods running and howling as fast as he could go.

Ned had done it! He had actually scared the bear away with his trusty nasal spray when Alex and Carlos and I had been too frightened to do anything. That's when we decided that maybe Ned was not such a nerd after all. As a matter of fact, Ned is going camping with us again next month, and this time we're all taking a bottle of nasal spray. You can't ever tell when you'll meet a bear with allergies!

Think carefully about each of the next questions. Although there are no right or wrong answers, your answers should make sense.

- At the end of the story, Donnie says that he and his friends are all going camping again in a month. Would you go camping again after the incident with the bear? ______________________________

____

- What would you have done to keep from being harmed by the bear?

____

____

Share your answers with a partner who has also read "Incident at Dickens Creek." Discuss why you did or didn't like the story.

Story Mapping

Answer the following questions to check how well you understood "Incident at Dickens Creek." These questions will help you remember the most important events in the story.

1. Where does the story take place?________________
2. Who are the main characters in the story?________________
____
3. Why is Donnie upset when his mother tells him that his cousin, Ned, is coming for a visit?________________
____
4. How does Ned behave on the camping trip?________________
____
5. What was outside the tent in the middle of the night?________________
____
6. Explain how Ned helps Donnie solve the problem.________________
____
7. How does the story end?________________
____

Check your answers in the answer key in the back of the book. The questions helped you think about the most important events from the beginning to the end of the story. Another way to explain the story's important events is to write a story map. The diagram below is an example of a story map. Notice how the questions you answered and the story map work together to retell important events in "Incident at Dickens Creek."

THE SETTING

Main Characters: **Donnie, Ned**
Place: **Dickens Creek**

First Important Event

Donnie's mother tells him that Aunt Dottie and Cousin Ned are coming for a visit.

Next

SNIFF!

Ned arrives—sneezing, wheezing and sniffing—and not too eager to go on a camping trip.

Next

Ned's behavior on the campout irritates Donnie and his friends.

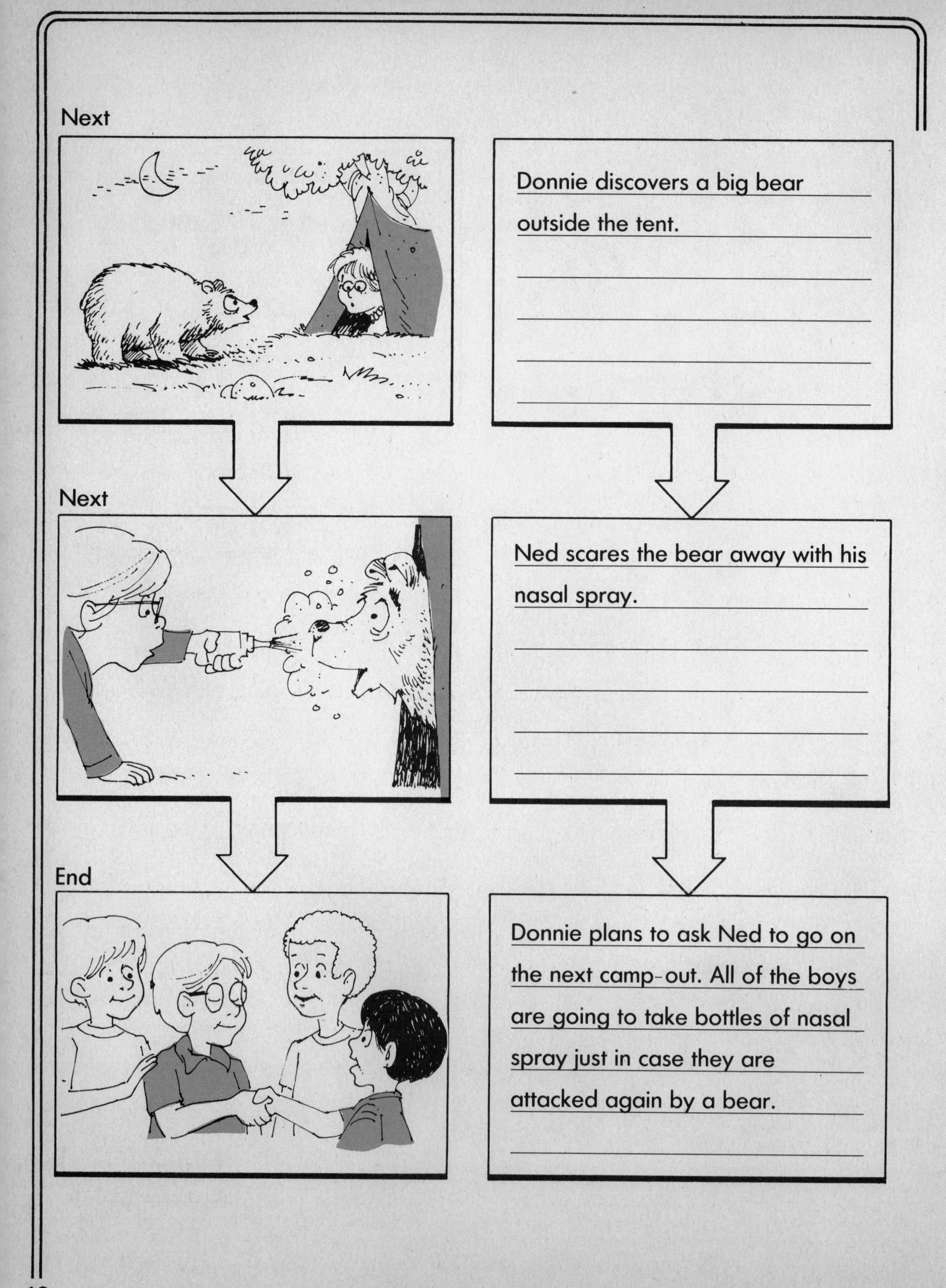
Next
Donnie discovers a big bear outside the tent.
Next
Ned scares the bear away with his nasal spray.
End
Donnie plans to ask Ned to go on the next camp-out. All of the boys are going to take bottles of nasal spray just in case they are attacked again by a bear.

You can see how story maps help you remember the most important events in a story. Use the completed story map to retell "The Incident at Dickens Creek" to a partner.

STEP BACK AND THINK Vocabulary Development

Answer the questions on the lines that follow.

1. Some words have different meanings to different people. In "Incident at Dickens Creek," Donnie and his friends think that Ned is a *nerd.* What is your definition of a *nerd?* ______________________________

   ____

   ____

2. What are some things Ned does to make the boys think that he is a nerd?

   ____

   ____

3. Ned doesn't act like a nerd at the end of the story. What words would you use to describe Ned when he saved the boys from the bear? ______________

   ____

   ____

4. The words listed below are characteristics that people might have. These characteristics are called **character traits.** Read each list of character traits. Write the name of the kind of person each list describes.

a. ______________

- picks on smaller people
- mean
- cowardly

b. ______________

- brave
- fearless
- risks his life to save others

c. ______________

- dishonest
- sneaky
- takes things that belong to others

Donnie describes Ned in unusual ways several times in "Incident at Dickens Creek." These unusual descriptions are called **figurative language.** Read the following examples from the story. Answer the questions on the lines that follow.

5. When Donnie tells about how Ned annoyed everyone on the campout, he says that Ned was *a real joy to have around.* What did Donnie really mean? ____

____

____

6. Donnie said that Ned's coming to visit made him *sick.* What did he really mean? ____

____

____

STEP OUT ON YOUR OWN **Writing**

The boys' experience with the bear at Dickens Creek would make a good news article. Pretend that you are a reporter for your school newspaper. Your job is to write the facts about what happened on the campout. Remember that all good news stories tell *Who, What, Where, When, Why* and *How* something happened. Make notes for your article in the space that follows.

Use your notes to write a news story. Before you begin, organize the facts so that they will make sense to your readers. Write a rough draft on the following lines.

Share your rough draft with your teacher or writing partners. Ask them what revisions should be made to make the article clearer. Use their suggestions when you write your next draft.

Lesson 2: THE LITTLE OLD LADY WHO LIKED SPIDERS

by Eileen Snyder

GET INTO STEP **Prior Knowledge**

1. Read each of the questions that follow. Then choose at least one to answer on the lines below.

- Do you like spiders? Explain your answer.
- What is the nicest surprise you ever received? Write a sentence or two about it.
- Have you ever given someone an unusual gift? Tell about it.

____

____

____

____

2. What do you think "The Little Old Lady Who Liked Spiders" is about? Make some predictions.

____

____

____

____

STEP INTO THE STORY **Guided Reading**

Read "The Little Old Lady Who Liked Spiders" to find out if any of your predictions are true. As you read the story, you will come to several breaking points. You will be asked to think, to react and to write.

Once there was a little old lady named Lolly who liked spiders. There were spider webs in every nook and cranny and corner of her house in every size, shape and design you could imagine. Some of the spiders were funnel weavers, and some were orb weavers and some were cobweb weavers. And there were also the wolf spiders and jumping spiders that didn't spin any webs at all, but could run with surprising speed along the floors, up the walls and even upside down over the ceilings.

When the little old lady cleaned house—which, truth to tell, wasn't all that often—she would very carefully look over each spider web just to make sure it was old and abandoned before she swept it up. If a spider was at home, the little old lady would wish her a good morning and clean off the spider's front stoop for her.

What kind of person is Lolly? Write some words to describe her. ____________

____

____

All through the summer, Lolly watched the mother spiders carefully guarding their egg sacs. And when the spiderlings hatched out, she saw swarms of baby spiders spreading out along their mothers' web lines. Then she watched the babies going off on their own little corners to spin their own little webs—all exactly like their mothers', but smaller. There were tiny funnels and tiny orbs and tiny cobwebs.

Now Christmas was coming and Lolly thought about putting up a Christmas tree. She rummaged around in the attic until, at last, under a big box of valentines, she found the Christmas ornaments. Because she didn't have much money, Lolly used the same decorations over and over again, year after year.

On Christmas Eve Lolly went out to buy a small tree, but by that time, nearly all the good ones had been taken. She finally found one, brought it home, and stood it on a table in a corner of the living room. And then even Lolly could see that it was a sad looking tree. She sighed a very deep sigh, and all the spider webs in the living room vibrated softly with her.

The living room seemed melancholy and depressing in spite of the tree.

In a little while, she turned out the lights and slowly climbed the stairs to her bedroom, her carpet slippers softly slap-slapping as she went from step to step.

Well, you know that every Christmas Eve a very fantastic and wonderful thing happens. On that one night of the year, all the animals are able to talk, and of course, spiders are no exception. At the stroke of midnight, they become regular chatterboxes.

Do you think that animals or insects ever talk to each other? ______________

Explain your answer. ____

____

____

The wolf spiders and the jumping spiders were the first to notice the sad little tree with its thread-bare decorations. Because these spiders stalk and catch their prey much as cats do, they have very keen eyes and little escapes their attention.

The news, however, had to be carried to the web weavers. They have rather poor eyesight and must depend on vibrations of their webs to find out what's what.

The spiders all liked the little old lady, because she was so very careful not to step on them or sweep them up. They thought and thought about what they might do to make this Christmas happy for her. Some said, "Why don't we give her a fly or two all wrapped up in spider silk?" This was the nicest thing they could think of. Flies were hard to get in the middle of winter, and the gift would be a real sacrifice for them. But others said, "No, we don't think that would be a good present because we've never seen her eat flies."

So they thought and thought and thought some more. What else did they have that Lolly might like? Then one jumping spider, whose name was Victoria, had an idea.

What do you think Victoria's idea will be? Make a prediction. ______________

____

____

"Tell the funnel weavers, the orb weavers and the cobweb weavers to come to the Christmas tree, she said to the other wolf spiders and jumping spiders.

They rushed to carry out Victoria's orders, and such a scurrying has seldom been seen as all the spiders, except the tiniest baby spiders, gathered together under the Christmas tree.

You could see that with her regal bearing Victoria made a very good chief engineer. Victoria directed all the funnel weavers, the orb weavers and the cobweb weavers to spread out over the Christmas tree and to start weaving their webs. The jumping spiders and the wolf spiders were to be the leaders.

Throughout the entire operation, Victoria was everywhere. She surveyed all the branches on the tree so she could tell where to place webs for the best effect. She examined the ornaments to see what might be done to refurbish them. Finally, she tested lines for tautness and strength and inspected finished webs for design and spacing.

At last, the tree was completely covered with silvery strands of spider webs that shone and shimmered softly in the moonlight. Every ornament was encased in a dainty, elegant web, or wrapped in fine spider silk that took on the color of the ornament: red, blue, green, silver or gold. The angels had new wings of gossamer, and the star at the top of the tree twinkled again.

The spiders had never seen anything more beautiful. As they climbed down the tree, they admired each other's work. They even had a compliment or two for the cobweb weavers; after all, it was now Christmas morning.

The sun shining into the window made the Christmas tree glow as red as fire. The spiders had returned to their home webs by this time—exhausted but happy.

What do you think Lolly will say when she sees the tree? Make a prediction.

____

____

____

____

Soon they heard the thump, thump of slippered feet. It was Lolly trudging down the stairs in her old blue flannel bathrobe. She stumped toward the kitchen, for she was never fully awake in the morning until she had a cup or two of coffee.

But today something startled her awake. She wheeled around and rubbed her eyes. She looked and rubbed them again. She could not believe what she saw. That couldn't be her Christmas tree! Not the little one she had put up only last night. This tree was beautiful; it glimmered and gleamed in the morning sunlight.

Lolly came closer and saw that the shining tree was covered with exquisite spider webs, woven in the most intricate designs. The spiders really had outdone themselves. There were cones and stars, circles and spirals, cones within cones, stars within stars, circles within circles, spirals within spirals. Spirals and cones were inside circles and stars; snowflakes were everywhere, and no two of them were alike.

Even the disorganized webs of the cobweb weavers, instead of distracting from the design, served as a kind of netting to bind the whole together.

Lolly laughed; she laughed so hard that tears streamed down her cheeks. She turned and smiled at all the corners and the doorways and the windows and at all the spider webs in their nooks and crannies that were now vibrating with happiness. Wiping her cheeks, she said, "Thank you, my friends, for the loveliest Christmas present I ever had."

And at the very top of the tree, sitting on the star in the radiance of the sun, Victoria nodded graciously.

Think carefully before answering these next questions. Although there are no right or wrong answers, your answers should make sense.

- What lesson can be learned from this story?

____

____

- Why do you think the little old lady was so fond of spiders?

____

____

Share your answers with a partner who has also read this story. Talk about the parts of the story you each liked best.

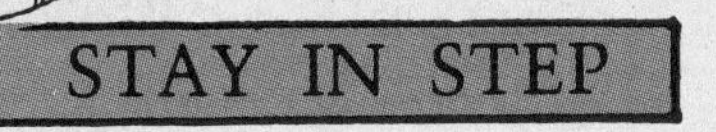

Story Mapping

Now that you have read "The Little Old Lady Who Liked Spiders" and discussed it with a partner, you are ready to answer questions about the important events in the story.

1. Where does the story take place? ______________________________
____
2. Who are the main characters in the story? ______________________________
____
3. What is the problem with Lolly's Christmas tree? ______________________________
____
4. Why do the spiders want to give Lolly a special Christmas present? ____________
____
____
5. Describe the gift Victoria suggests the spiders give to Lolly. ______________
____
____
6. What does Lolly do when she sees her present? ______________________________
____

Check your answers by looking in the answer key in the back of the book. A story map for "The Little Old Lady Who Liked Spiders" has been started for you. In the boxes on the left, make a drawing or write key words to help you remember the order of the events in the story. Complete the story map. Use the questions as a guide if you need help.

THE SETTING

Main Characters: **Lolly, Victoria**
Place: **Lolly's house**

First Important Event

Lolly buys a small Christmas tree and decorates it with a few old, worn–out ornaments.

Next

gift

The spiders try to think of a gift to give Lolly because she has always treated them so kindly.

Next

End

Does your map include all the important events that happened in the story? Using your map, retell "The Little Old Lady Who Liked Spiders" to a partner who has mapped the same story.

QUIET! SUPERMIND AT WORK!

STEP BACK AND THINK **Vocabulary Development**

In "The Little Old Lady Who Liked Spiders," the author uses some words and phrases that may be new to you. However, you can figure out what they mean by the way they are used in the story. This is called **context.**

1. When Lolly first put up her tree on Christmas Eve, the author says that it made the whole room seem *melancholy.* Draw a circle around the word that best describes the meaning of *melancholy.*
   old empty frightening sad
2. The author says that Victoria's *regal bearing* would make her a good chief engineer. On the lines below, describe the behavior of someone with *regal bearing.*

3. Think of someone you know who has *regal bearing.* Write a sentence about that person.

Similes compare two things by using *like* or *as.* In "The Little Old Lady Who Liked Spiders," the author uses a simile in this sentence:

The sun shining into the window made
the Christmas tree glow *as red as fire.*

What two things are being compared? How are those two things alike? Complete the following similes. The first two have been done for you.

- as black as **night**
- **prances** like a bull

4. as bright as ______________________
5. as ______________________ as a bullet
6. ______________________ like a tree
7. runs like a ______________________
8. dirty as a ______________________
9. ______________________ as a kitten

STEP OUT ON YOUR OWN — Writing

In "The Little Old Lady Who Liked Spiders," Victoria and the other spiders were able to talk on Christmas Eve. What if animals really could talk? What would be the advantages and disadvantages? Make some notes on the following lines.

Advantages	Disadvantages
______________________________	______________________________
______________________________	______________________________
______________________________	______________________________
______________________________	______________________________
______________________________	______________________________

Decide whether you think talking animals would make the world a better or a worse place. Write a rough paragraph supporting your opinion. Try to convince classmates that you are right by giving them reasons to prove your point. Begin your paragraph in the space that follows. Use another piece of paper to finish.

____

____

____

____

____

____

____

____

____

____

Share the paragraph with your writing partners. Find out if your writing persuaded them that your opinion is right. Get ideas for making your paragraph even more persuasive when you revise.

Lesson 3: THE NEW HAMPSHIRE KIDNAPPING

by Daniel Cohen

GET INTO STEP Prior Knowledge

1. Read each of the following questions carefully. Answer at least one question on the lines below.

- Has something really strange ever happened to you? Write a sentence about what happened.
- Has anyone ever told you something that was very hard to believe? What was it?
- Have you or anyone you know ever seen a UFO? Tell what happened.

____

____

____

____

2. Make some predictions about "The New Hampshire Kidnapping."

____

____

____

____

STEP INTO THE STORY Guided Reading

Read "The New Hampshire Kidnapping" to find out if any of your predictions are true. As you read the story, you will come to several breaking points. You will be asked to think, to react and to write.

On the night of 19 September 1961, Barney and Betty Hill were on their way home to Portsmouth, New Hampshire, after a short vacation in Canada. The drive took them down a deserted highway through the White Mountains. At about ten o'clock the Hills thought they saw a bright object in the sky. It seemed to be following their car!

The couple's dachshund became restless, and Betty suggested they stop the car and walk her. Barney grabbed a pair of binoculars and looked at the object in the sky. But he couldn't make out what it was.

What do you think the object is? Make a prediction. ______________________

____

____

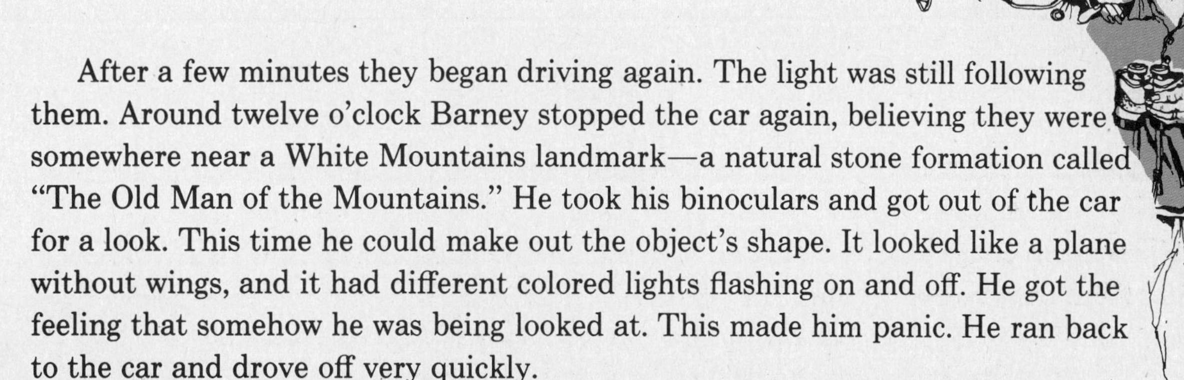

After a few minutes they began driving again. The light was still following them. Around twelve o'clock Barney stopped the car again, believing they were somewhere near a White Mountains landmark—a natural stone formation called "The Old Man of the Mountains." He took his binoculars and got out of the car for a look. This time he could make out the object's shape. It looked like a plane without wings, and it had different colored lights flashing on and off. He got the feeling that somehow he was being looked at. This made him panic. He ran back to the car and drove off very quickly.

About two hours later, Barney saw a road sign. He figured he was about thirty-five miles from where he had last looked at the object in the sky. But neither he nor Betty could remember anything about the drive. They didn't know why it had taken them so long to go only thirty-five miles. It was as if they had "lost" two hours of their lives.

What could have happened to Barney and Betty? ______________________

____

About ten days later Betty began having nightmares about being kidnapped by creatures from another planet. She couldn't remember the dreams very well, but even after she woke up she felt scared. Although the dreams stopped in a week, Betty continued to worry about them.

Barney didn't have bad dreams, but he did feel sick and upset. He got headaches and had trouble sleeping and felt very tired during the day. He went to a local doctor, who tried for a year to find out what was wrong with him. The doctor knew that something was weighing on Barney's mind, but he didn't know what it was, and Barney didn't know either. Finally the doctor suggested that both Barney and Betty visit Dr. Benjamin Simon, a specialist and expert hypnotist who treated people with mental problems.

Have you ever been hypnotized? ______________________________

If not, what do you think it would be like? ______________________

____

The Hills saw Dr. Simon in December, 1963. They went back to see him many times, and he hypnotized both of them separately. While under hypnosis, people sometimes remember things they don't remember in a conscious state, and Barney and Betty each told an amazing story about what had happened on the night of 19 September during those "lost" hours:

They were badly frightened by the thing in the sky—though they weren't sure why. They tried to drive away from it but got lost. As they drove down a side road, they saw flashing lights ahead and a group of figures standing by the road, signaling them to stop. Barney first thought the lights were flashing to warn motorists of an accident and that the figures were policemen. But they weren't. The lights came from a spaceship that had landed near the road, and the figures were from the spaceship.

Barney couldn't remember exactly what the figures looked like. He said they wore black jackets, and one reminded him of "a red-headed Irishman." Betty's description was clearer. She said the figures had strange insectlike faces, with large slanting eyes and big lipless mouths. Barney drew some pictures of what he thought the creatures looked like, and his pictures fit Betty's description.

Think about the description you've just read. Use it to make a sketch of what you think the space creatures looked like. Use the space below.

The Hills said they cooperated with the creatures and were released unharmed. When they got back to their car, they found their dog asleep inside. They had been told by the creatures that they wouldn't remember what had happened. And, in fact, they didn't remember any of the details until they were hypnotized by Dr. Simon.

What do you think the Hills must have felt when they realized what had happened to them? Write some words to describe their feelings. ____________

____

____

____

The Hills talked about their experience with many people. They even contacted groups dedicated to proving that UFOs are spaceships. But they didn't try to make money by telling their story. Other people who claim to have contacted creatures from UFOs have tried to make money or get publicity. This makes critics of UFOs very suspicious. But most of the people who talked to the Hills were convinced that Barney and Betty were honest and that they really had had an experience they couldn't explain.

The Hill case is probably the best known UFO encounter in the world today. But did it take place as the Hills described it? Let's look at the details a little more closely.

First, there is no physical evidence for the encounter. No one else in the area reported a UFO, and radar stations in New Hampshire didn't track any unusual objects on the night of 19 September 1961. The only evidence we have is what the Hills said.

Second, most people think the Hills were honest—that they were telling what they thought was the truth. But did they describe what actually happened? Perhaps not. The full story of the meeting with the space people only came out under hypnosis. It's a mistaken notion that a hypnotized person must tell the truth. That isn't so. A hypnotized person may tell what he or she thinks is the truth. But it may not be what actually happened. In fact, Dr. Simon doesn't think the Hills were taken aboard a spaceship. Yet he doesn't think they were lying when they told the story. How can this be?

How can the Hills be telling the truth if they didn't have an encounter with the spaceship? ______________________________

____

____

Dr. Simon believes that the Hills did see a bright object in the sky. They thought it was a spaceship and became frightened. After they got home, Betty Hill began to have nightmares about being taken aboard an alien spaceship. It didn't really happen, but she thought it did; dreams can seem very real. Dr. Simon thinks she described her dreams to Barney and gradually made him believe them, too. When they were hypnotized, both described Betty's dreams. But by that time both were convinced that what she had dreamed about had actually happened.

Have you ever had a dream that seemed so real you thought it actually happened? If so, write a sentence about it. ______________________________

____

____

Third, what took place during the two "lost" hours? Well, are we sure there really were two "lost" hours? The Hills didn't know exactly what time it was when they stopped to look at the UFO. Then they got lost and drove around in the dark for a while—we don't know how long. So they may have just been mistaken about the time. It is an easy mistake to make, particularly if you are scared. And the Hills were very scared.

That is where the famous Hill case stands today. Was the New Hampshire couple actually kidnapped and taken aboard a UFO? Or was the whole thing a trick of the human mind? You must make up your own mind about that.

Think very carefully about these next questions. There are no right or wrong answers, but your answers should make sense.

- Think about what you've just read about the Hills. Do you believe that they were kidnapped and taken aboard a spaceship? ______________________________

  ____

- How do you think your life would change if you had an experience like Barney and Betty Hill? ______________________________

  ____

  ____

  ____

Share your answers with someone who has also read "The New Hampshire Kidnapping." Discuss your feelings about the story.

STAY IN STEP **Story Mapping**

In Lesson 2 you completed a story map for "The Little Old Lady Who Liked Spiders." The questions you answered helped you recall the main events in the story. In this lesson you will not find any questions. Instead, *ask yourself* questions about the most important events in "The New Hampshire Kidnapping." In the boxes on the left, make a drawing or write key words to help you remember the order of the events in the story. Then complete the story map that has been started for you. Remember — a story map includes only the most important events needed to retell a story. You may not always need all the spaces that are provided.

THE SETTING

Main Characters: **Barney and Betty Hill**

Place: **New Hampshire**

First Important Event

On their way home from a vacation, Betty and Barney Hill feel like they are being followed by a bright object resembling a spaceship.

Next

nightmares

Betty begins to have nightmares about being kidnapped, and Barney feels upset and sick.

Next

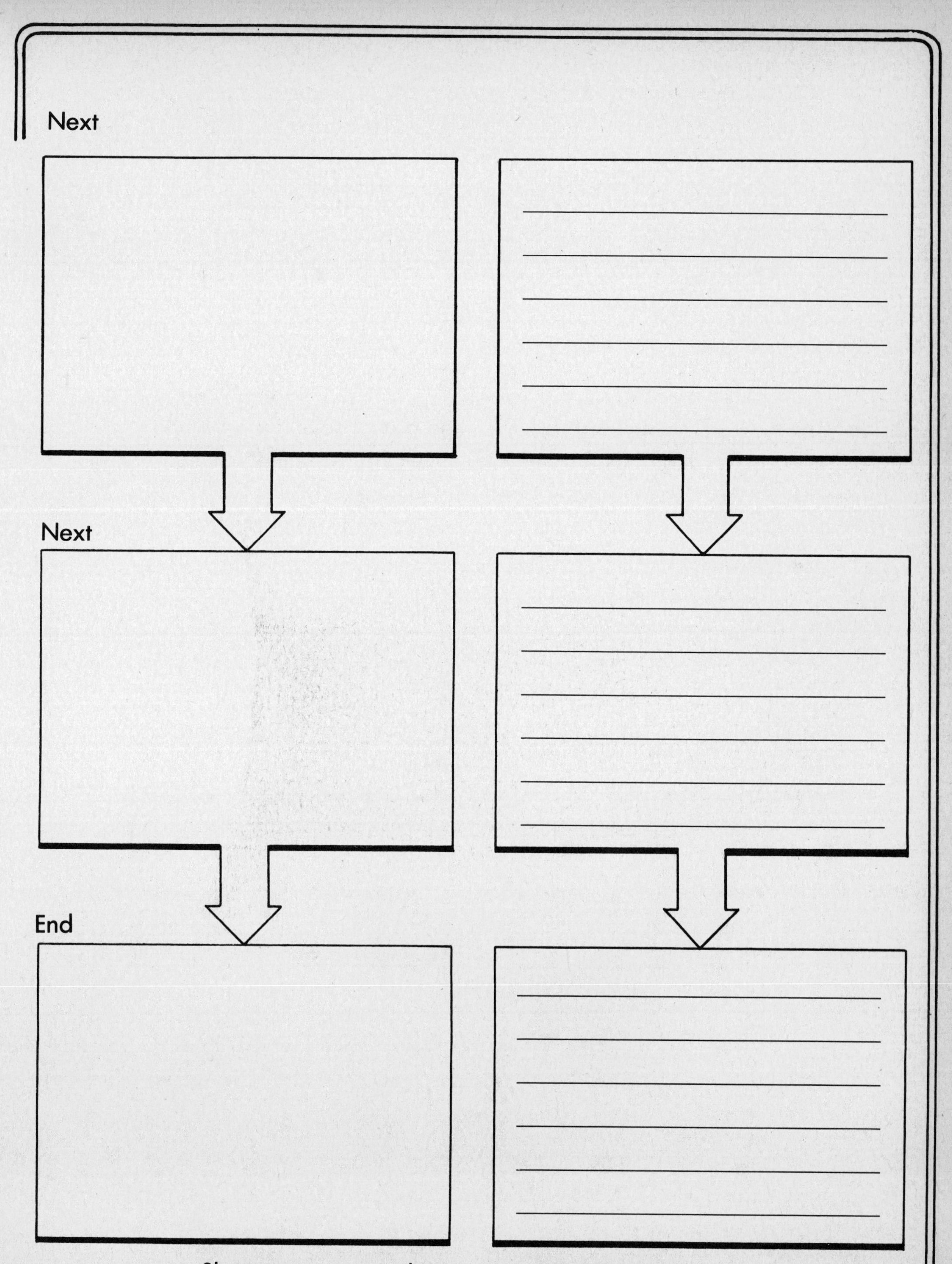

Share your map with a partner who has also mapped the story. How are your maps alike? How are they different? Use them to retell the story.

Vocabulary Development

People sometimes use colorful or descriptive words to say what they mean. You have learned that this is called **figurative language.**

1. In "The New Hampshire Kidnapping," the author says that after the experience with the UFO, Barney had something *weighing on his mind.*

   What do you think the author means? ______________________________

   ____

   ____

   ____

2. Think of a time when something was weighing on your mind. Write a sentence about it. ______________________________

   ____

   ____

   ____

Writers often use words in ways that explain how they feel about a person or thing. Some words suggest a pleasant meaning and others suggest an unpleasant meaning. These meanings are called **connotations.** For example:

My dog is plump.
My dog is fat.

You know that *plump* and *fat* have similar meanings. However, which sentence has a more pleasant connotation?

____

Read each set of sentences. Write *most pleasant* or *most unpleasant* on the lines that follow.

3. Barney panicked when he saw the UFO. ______________________
4. Barney worried when he saw the UFO. ______________________
5. The space creatures had strange features. ______________________
6. The space creatures had grotesque features. ______________________

Read each of the following sentences. Place a check beside the answers.

7. Lisa was unhappy that the party had been cancelled.
   Betsy was miserable that the party had been cancelled.
   Who probably felt more upset?

   _____ Lisa _____ Betsy

8. Tom's baseball uniform was filthy.
   Greg's baseball uniform was soiled.
   Who probably had the dirtiest uniform?

   _____ Tom _____ Greg

9. Mom was delighted to see that I'd cleaned my room.
   Grandma was pleased to see that I'd cleaned my room.
   Who probably acted happier?

   _____ Mom _____ Grandma

STEP OUT ON YOUR OWN   Writing

Imagine what it would be like to meet an alien from another planet. Write a story about just such a happening. Describe how the alien looks. Explain how it communicates with you and whether or not it is friendly. Tell why it came to Earth and what it wants from you. Make some notes on the following lines.

Choose your favorite ideas for your story. As you write, be sure to use words that describe the alien and your feelings about it. You may begin your rough draft in the space below. Use another piece of paper to finish. Be sure to give your story a title.

Share your story with your teacher or a partner. Find out what they like best about the story and get their ideas for improving your next draft.

Lesson 4: THE PERFECT HIDING PLACE

by Sheila Stroup

GET INTO STEP **Prior Knowledge**

1. Read each of the following questions. Answer at least one question on the lines that follow.

- Did you ever play hide–and–seek when you were younger? Tell about it.
- Think of a time when you were afraid that you might be hurt. What happened?
- Have you ever had a good idea that turned out to be a bad one instead? Write a sentence or two about what happened.

____

____

____

____

2. Make some predictions about "The Perfect Hiding Place."

____

____

____

____

STEP INTO THE STORY **Guided Reading**

Read "The Perfect Hiding Place" to find out if any of your predictions are true. As you read the story, you will come to several breaking points. You will be asked to think, to react and to write.

When I was eight and my brother Larry was twelve, one of our favorite rainy-day pastimes was playing hide-and-seek indoors. We lived in a big old three-story house that my grandfather had built forty years earlier. The house creaked and groaned like a person in pain, and it had many shadowy corners, dark closets, and large, old pieces of furniture to hide under or behind.

Have you ever been in a place like this one? _____ If so, write about it. _____

____

The only thing I did not like about playing hide-and-seek was that, although I had much better hiding places, Larry could always find me, and I could never find him. Whether I was under my parents' bed or in back of the davenport, behind the drapes or even in the pantry, hiding among the stacks of newspapers we saved for the Boy Scouts' paper drive, Larry always found me. But he would hide in the simplest places—behind the bathroom door or in the cubbyhole beneath our father's desk—and somehow I would overlook him.

Only once did Larry have a truly inventive hiding place. He took the screen out of his bedroom window, climbed out onto the front porch roof and waited there in the rain. By the time I finally found him, a half-hour later, he was shivering. His red hair was plastered down flat against his head, and rivulets of water were running down into his face.

"This is the best hiding place yet," he said, grinning wetly, and I knew he was right.

What is the best hiding place you've ever had? _____________________

____

"I'm telling Mom," I said, so he wouldn't feel quite so smug about outsmarting me. But he promised to let me wear his Wild Bill Hickok belt that glowed in the dark, the next time we went to the movies, and I agreed to keep my mouth shut.

After that day I knew I had to come up with a hiding place where Larry wouldn't ever find me. It had to be in a place I'd never chosen before, a place Larry would never think of looking.

Make a prediction about the hiding place. Where do you think it will be? ____

____

Keep reading to find out if you're right.

One rainy Saturday afternoon, while Larry was taking his drum lesson, I decided to find the perfect place. I started looking in the kitchen. My mother was making cookies and listening to the opera on the radio.

"What are you looking for?" she asked me.

"I'm looking for a place to hide where Larry can't find me," I explained.

"How about in back of those stacks of newspapers in the pantry?" my mother suggested.

"He already found me there."

"Humm. Why don't you try behind the drapes in back of the davenport?" she asked.

"He already found me there, too," I said with a sigh.

"Maybe," said my mother, "you need to find a place so simple, he would never think of looking there."

"Sure, Mom," I said.

Then I went into my own room and sat down on my bed to think. I looked all around—at the closet, which was just like Larry's, at the radiator in the corner, which made a hungry gurgling noise, and at a painted orange crate filled with stuffed animals and picture books. There were no hiding places anywhere.

Suddenly I looked straight ahead. My dresser! It was a huge, ancient dresser that had belonged to my grandparents. It was made of wood so heavy and dark that it looked black in the afternoon shadows. I used only the top two drawers for my clothes. The third drawer, I found, was full of winter blankets. I closed it and pulled hard on the two handles of the big bottom drawer. It was empty. Perfect! I thought and tried lying down in it!

To get the drawer closed, I placed my hands flat against the bottom of the drawer above me and pushed slowly, slowly. The ceiling of my room disappeared, and I was shut inside the dresser.

Aha, he'll never find me here, I thought as I stared into the blackness. Soon I realized, however, that I did not like being shut up in the dark dresser at all. It smelled like a damp forest full of toadstools and vultures and screeching bats. I put my hands flat against the drawer above me and pushed again—slowly, slowly. Nothing happened. I pushed harder. The drawer would not budge. I frantically pushed harder. Still, nothing happened. I could hear my heart beating all the way up inside my ears.

Oh, no, he'll never find me here, I thought. No one will ever find me.

How do you think the girl feels now? Write some words to describe how you would feel if you were trapped inside the drawer.

______________ ______________ ______________

______________ ______________ ______________

"MOM!" I yelled in a voice so loud it made me jump. "MOM-M-M-M."

Did I hear footsteps, or just my own heartbeats? After an eternity, I heard my mother's voice. "Sheila?" she called out. "Sheila, where are you?"

"In the bottom drawer," I answered.

Then I heard a small grunt and saw a sliver of light as the drawer began to open. My mother stood above me, shaking her head. She helped me out of the drawer, and I noticed my brother Larry standing beside her.

"I couldn't get the drawer to open again," I said with a sick smile.

"That was really dumb," said Larry, but he wasn't being mean—just worried.

"I know it was dumb," I said.

My mother hugged me. "Promise me that you'll never get inside something again unless you're sure you can get back out."

"I promise."

After my heart had stopped beating in my ears, we went down to the kitchen for some milk and cookies.

"Want to play hide-and-seek?" Larry asked when we were through eating.

"O.K.," I said, jumping up. He closed his eyes, and I ran up to my room as quickly and quietly as I could and sat down on my bed to think. It was cold in my room, so I lay down on my bed and pulled the quilt up around me. The bed felt wonderfully soft and warm, and I decided to just lie there and think for a minute.

Then I heard Larry running up the stairs. I hunched down at the foot of the bed and covered my head with the quilt. First I heard him open the bathroom clothes hamper. Next he looked in the linen closet. Now he was in my room. He turned the closet light on. Finally he opened and closed each dresser drawer. I held my breath. Now he was walking back down the hall—then I heard his footsteps on the stairs.

A few minutes later he called up from the landing, "Allie, allie, all out are in free!" I jumped out of bed and quietly moved across my room.

"Where were you?" Larry asked as I came down the steps. "I looked everywhere."

"I found the perfect hiding place," I said. "And I'm not telling you where it is."

And I never did.

Think about these next questions. Even though there are no right or wrong answers, your answers should make sense.

- Why do you think Larry couldn't find Sheila when she hid under the covers on her bed?

____

____

- What do you think is the most important lesson that Sheila learned from her experiences?

____

____

Share your answers with a partner who has also read "The Perfect Hiding Place." Talk about how your answers are alike and how they are different.

Story Mapping

Before completing the story map in Lesson 3, you *asked yourself* questions about the important events in the story. In this lesson you will do the same thing. Use your questions to write a story map. In the boxes on the left, make a drawing or write key words to help you remember the order of the events in the story. You may not always need all the spaces that are provided. Be sure to include information about the setting.

THE SETTING

Main Characters:

Place:

First Important Event
Next
Next

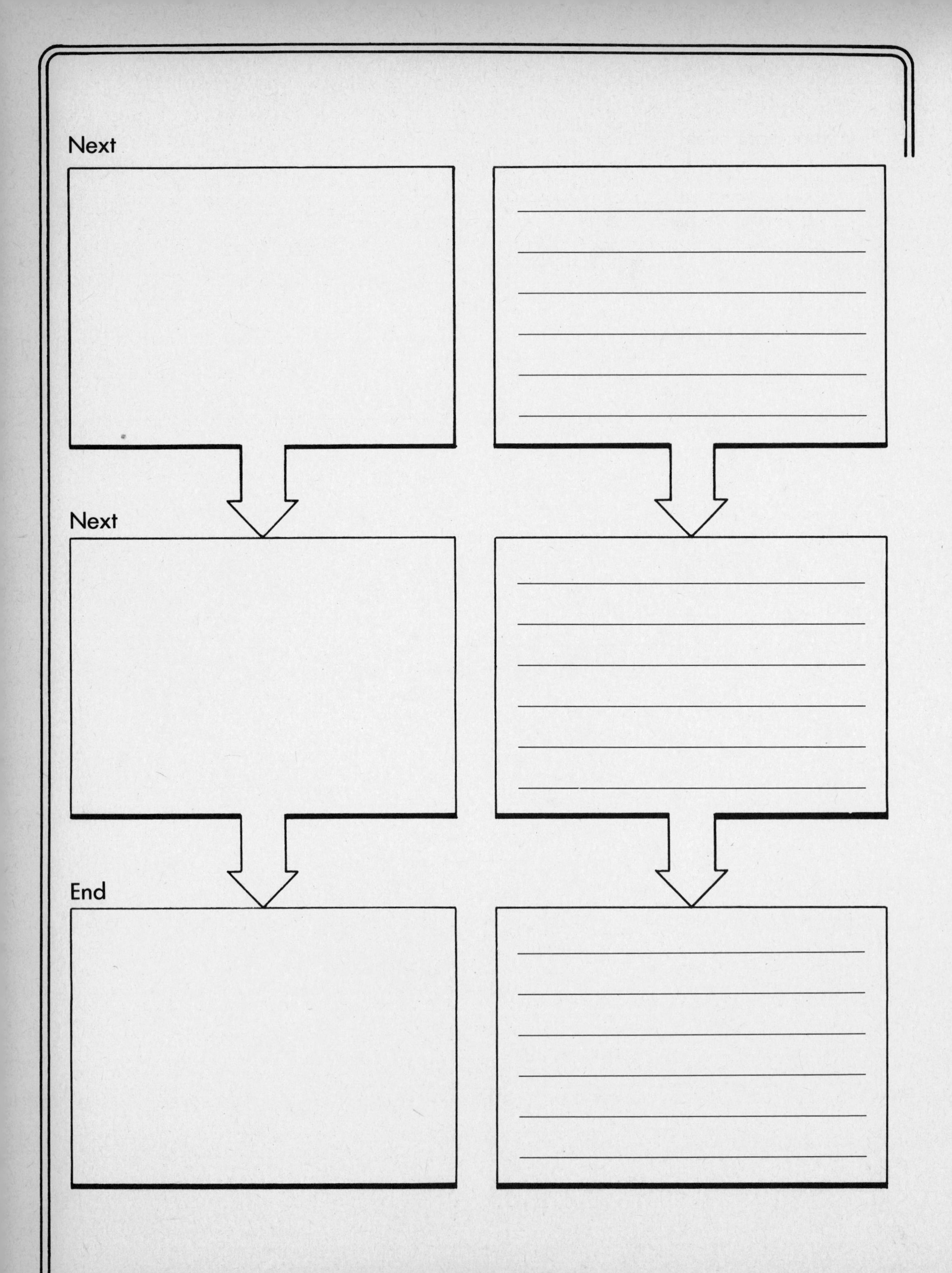
Next
Next
End

Share your map with a partner who has also mapped the story. How are your maps alike? How are they different? Use them to retell "The Perfect Hiding Place." Did the maps help you and your partner retell the important events in the story? If so, both maps are correct, even if they are different.

STEP BACK AND THINK Vocabulary Development

The author uses some excellent similes to describe some of the hiding places in "The Perfect Hiding Place." Remember that **similes** compare two things by using *like* or *as.* Answer the questions on the lines that follow.

1. When Sheila Stroup describes the old house in the story, she says that it "creaked and groaned like a person in pain." What two things are being compared? How are those two things alike? ____________________

   ____

   ____

2. Another simile in the story describes the drawer that the main character was trapped inside.

   "It smelled like a damp forest full of
   toadstools and vultures and screeching bats."

   What two things are being compared? What does this simile tell you about how the girl felt when she was inside the drawer? ____________________

   ____

3. Similes can be used to make your own writing more interesting. Write some similes to describe each of the following situations. The first ones have been done for you.

Situation	Simile
the taste of something you like	**It tastes like paradise.**
the taste of something you don't like	**It tastes like old shoe leather.**

a.	a hat you think is pretty	It looks like a __________.
b.	a hat you think is ugly	It looks like a __________.
c.	a place that makes you happy	This place makes me feel as __ __________________.
d.	a place that makes you sad	This place makes me feel as __ __________________.
e.	a day you enjoy	This day ______________.
f.	a day you don't enjoy	This day ______________.
g.	a book you thought was exciting	That book ____________.
h.	a book you thought was boring	That book ____________.

You may not be familiar with some of the words used in "The Perfect Hiding Place." However, you should be able to figure out their meanings by noticing how they are used in the story. You have learned that this is called **context.**

4. The girl in the story thinks her brother feels *smug* when he hides on the roof. What do you think she means? Use the context of the sentence to determine the meaning of *smug.* Write your answer on the following lines. __________

____

____

5. Think of a time when you felt *smug* about something. Write a sentence about it on the line below. Be sure to use *smug* in your sentence. __________

____

____

6. The girl in the story says she hid in back of the *davenport.* On the lines below, write some words that mean the same as *davenport.* Remember to use the context of the sentence.

______________________ ______________________

STEP OUT ON YOUR OWN — Writing

In "The Perfect Hiding Place" the author tells about being trapped inside a drawer and afraid that she wouldn't get out. Everyone has had a time when something happened that caused strong feelings. Think of a time when you were very frightened or very happy or very angry about something. Choose one experience that you remember and describe what happened and how you felt.

Make some notes on the lines that follow. ______________________________

____

____

____

____

____

Decide which of the ideas you will use to describe your experience. Remember, also, how useful similes can be to help your audience understand what you are describing. Start your rough draft in the space that follows. Use another piece of paper if you need more room.

____

____

____

____

____

____

____

____

____

____

Share your rough draft with one or more writing partners. Get their ideas for any revisions that can make your writing even better.

Lesson 5: DEAR AUNT HELEN

by Helen S. Munro

GET INTO STEP Prior Knowledge

1. Think about each of the following questions. Answer at least one on the lines below.

- Think of a time when you had to do something you didn't want to do. Write a sentence about it.
- Have you ever had a pen pal? If so, write about him or her.
- Have you ever received a letter from someone? How did you feel about it?

____

____

____

2. Make some predictions about "Dear Aunt Helen." What do you think it will be about?

____

____

____

____

STEP INTO THE STORY Guided Reading

Read the story to find out if your predictions are true. As you read the story, you will come to several breaking points. You will be asked to think, to react and to write.

"What does Miss Touchin think I am—a robot?" muttered Joseph as he trudged home from school. "Write, write, write. First a report on snails, then Indians, and now she wants me to write letters to some old lady in a retirement home. I'll have to waste my whole weekend trying to think of what to say to someone I don't even know!"

Would you like to write to someone you've never met? Explain your answer.

____

____

Letting himself in the front door and dropping his book bag with a thump, Joseph headed for the cookie tin that his grandmother had sent from Italy. Scooping up his baseball and glove, he ran out the back door with a handful of cookies. First he'd play ball with his friends. The letter could wait till Sunday.

A light was on in the kitchen, and the delicious smell of spaghetti sauce greeted him when he came home for supper. "Hi, Joseph. Dinner is ready." His mother turned as he came into the kitchen. He ducked under her arm, and her welcoming kiss just missed its mark. Ever since his father had gone back to Italy to see the grandparents and sell the family stonecarving business, Joseph's mother seemed to kiss him a lot.

Joseph was hungry, and the spaghetti tasted great. "Supper was really good, Mom," he told her as he helped with the dishes. He liked working in the kitchen. Cooking was fun, and he didn't even mind cleaning up.

"As your father would say, some of us are lucky enough to be born Italian. Everybody else just eats Italian." His mother laughed as she folded her apron. "Well, now, how much homework do you have for Monday? We'll be busy at the shop tomorrow, and we're going to Uncle Antonio's farm after mass on Sunday, so you better do your lessons tonight."

Rats, thought Joseph, I can't even put it off until Sunday. Out loud he said, "Just a letter for English."

"Then get to it," answered his mother.

The moment had come. He got out his pencil and paper and looked at the name: *Mrs. Helen Smith.* Might as well get it over with.

Dear Mrs. Smith,

My name is Joseph and I am nine years old. I am in the third grade. I would like to be your pen pal.

Sincerely,
Joseph Bellini

What do you think of Joseph's letter? Write a sentence explaining your opinion. ______________________________

____

____

That says it all. How much more would an old lady want to know about a little kid, mused Joseph? Especially me.

The weekend went quickly, and on Monday Miss Touchin found only one mistake in Joseph's letter. He copied it over in his neatest handwriting, mailed it, and forgot about it.

About a week later, Joseph found a letter in the mailbox, addressed to Master Joseph Bellini. "That's me!" he shouted—and tore it open immediately.

Dear Joseph,

I am eighty-one years old and not in the third grade. I live in a retirement home with a lot of other ladies. Our building is all on one floor, and my room has a door that goes outside to a small patio. I planted petunias today, and I'm going to invite everyone to a party in my petunia patch.

The ladies here are nice but a little dull. What do you do for fun?

Sincerely,
H. Smith

P.S. Please call me Aunt Helen, as my nieces, great-nieces and nephews, and assorted friends do. Mrs. Smith sounds like the name of a pie!

Joseph was excited about his letter and took it to school the next day. What a mistake!

What do you think Joseph's teacher will say about the letter from Mrs. Smith? Make a prediction. ____________________

____

____

____

"Well, write her another letter," said Miss Touchin. "Show it to me before you send it, and I'll give you some extra credit in English for it."

Rats and double rats, more writing, thought Joseph. But somehow Aunt Helen sounded better than Mrs. Smith.

How would you feel if you had to write another letter to Aunt Helen? ____________________

____

____

Dear Aunt Helen,

I'm glad you are out of the third grade. I wish I were. My baseball team finally won a game. I hit the ball and a dog grabbed it and ran away. I scored the only run, and without the ball we couldn't play.

Sincerely, your pen pal,
Joseph

P.S. That's what I do for fun. Baseball, not school.

A week went by and another letter came.

Dear Joseph,

I'm glad to hear that your team won, sneaky as it was. Some of the ladies here feel about this place as you feel about school. Their children put them here. I have passed out all the lipsticks I got for Christmas to try to make them look cheerier.

I feel that I am lucky. My husband and I had no children, and I am here because it is a good place for me. I get three meals a day, and when they have liver, they don't make me eat it.

Love, your friend,
Aunt Helen

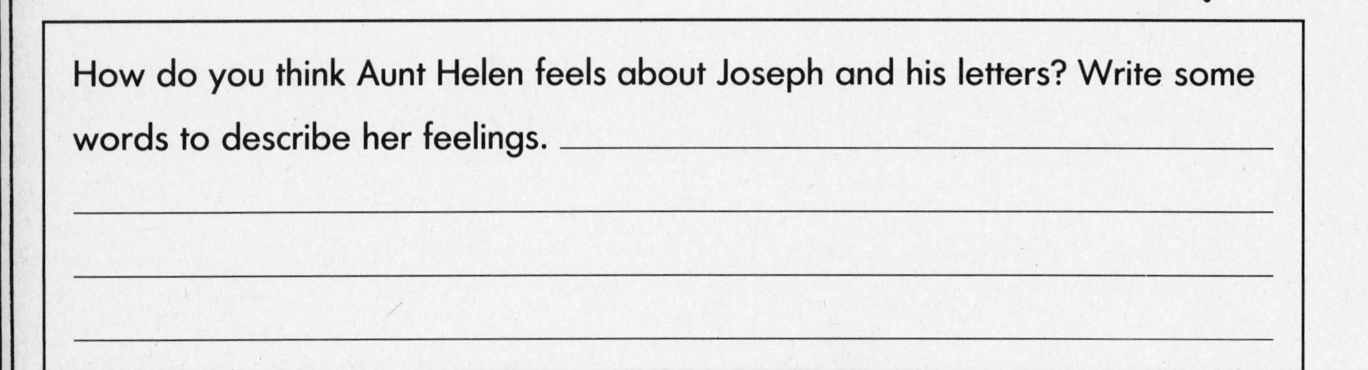

How do you think Aunt Helen feels about Joseph and his letters? Write some words to describe her feelings. ______________________________

____

____

____

Dear Aunt Helen,

Thanks for the letter. My mom got a letter today, too. My dad is in Italy, and my grandfather died. Now I have just my grandma, who will come to live with us. My mom cried and cried.

How are you? Will dying hurt?

Love, your friend,
Joseph

Dear Joseph,

I've been so busy living, Joseph, that I don't know if dying hurts or not. My husband was in pain one moment and dead the next. His face looked young and peaceful and definitely without pain.

My pain after he died was great, and I guess I can say that death is not painful but living can be. Give your mom a hug. It helps the hurt.

Love,
Aunt Helen

When his mom got home that night, Joseph was in the kitchen. He had the salad routine down pat from helping his mother, but he had just read the directions for making a "puffy omelet." He separated the eggs and then whipped the egg whites until he thought his arms would fall off. After carefully putting them together, he poured what he was sure was a mess into the hot, buttered pan. To his amazement, the omelet puffed up just as the cookbook had said it would.

His mother was flabbergasted. "Thank you, Joseph." She seemed to laugh and cry at the same time. "Great news! We're picking up Dad and Grandma at the airport tonight."

The plane was fifteen minutes late, and Joseph fidgeted until it landed. His dad came down the ramp looking tired and somehow smaller than Joseph remembered. Holding onto his arm was a black-haired lady with sad eyes.

How do you think Joseph and his grandmother will get along? Make a prediction about what will happen next. ______________________________

____

____

____

Joseph and his grandmother became friends in no time. In a few days he was teaching her English, and she helped him with his Italian. Sometimes he sounded just like his teacher: "Now try it again. You'll get it."

His letter to Aunt Helen that week was a little longer than usual.

Dear Aunt Helen,

My grandmother is sixty-one, but her English is about third grade. I think she must look like you. Let me know when your petunia patch blooms, and we'll come to see you.

My teacher says my writing has really improved. When she asked who has been helping me, I said, "Aunt Helen." She gave me a strange look. She knows my family. I never told her we are still pen pals. Every guy needs at least one secret, and I guess you're mine.

Love,
Joseph

P.S. I tried the lipstick on my grandmother. You're right. It makes older people look cheerier.

Think carefully before you answer these next questions. Although there are no right or wrong answers, your answers should make sense.

- Why do you think Joseph made dinner for his mother? ______________________

____

____

____

- Take a minute to think about Joseph. Do you think he learned any lessons from Aunt Helen? Explain your answer. ______________________

____

____

____

____

Share your answers with someone who has also read "Dear Aunt Helen." Discuss the story and your answers.

STAY IN STEP **Story Mapping**

Before completing the story map in Lesson 4, you questioned yourself about the most important events in the story. Now ask yourself questions about the main events in "Dear Aunt Helen" and write a story map in the shapes that are drawn. In the boxes on the left, make a drawing or write key words to help you remember the order of the events in the story. You may not always need all the shapes that are provided. Be certain to include information about the setting.

THE SETTING

Main Characters:

Place:

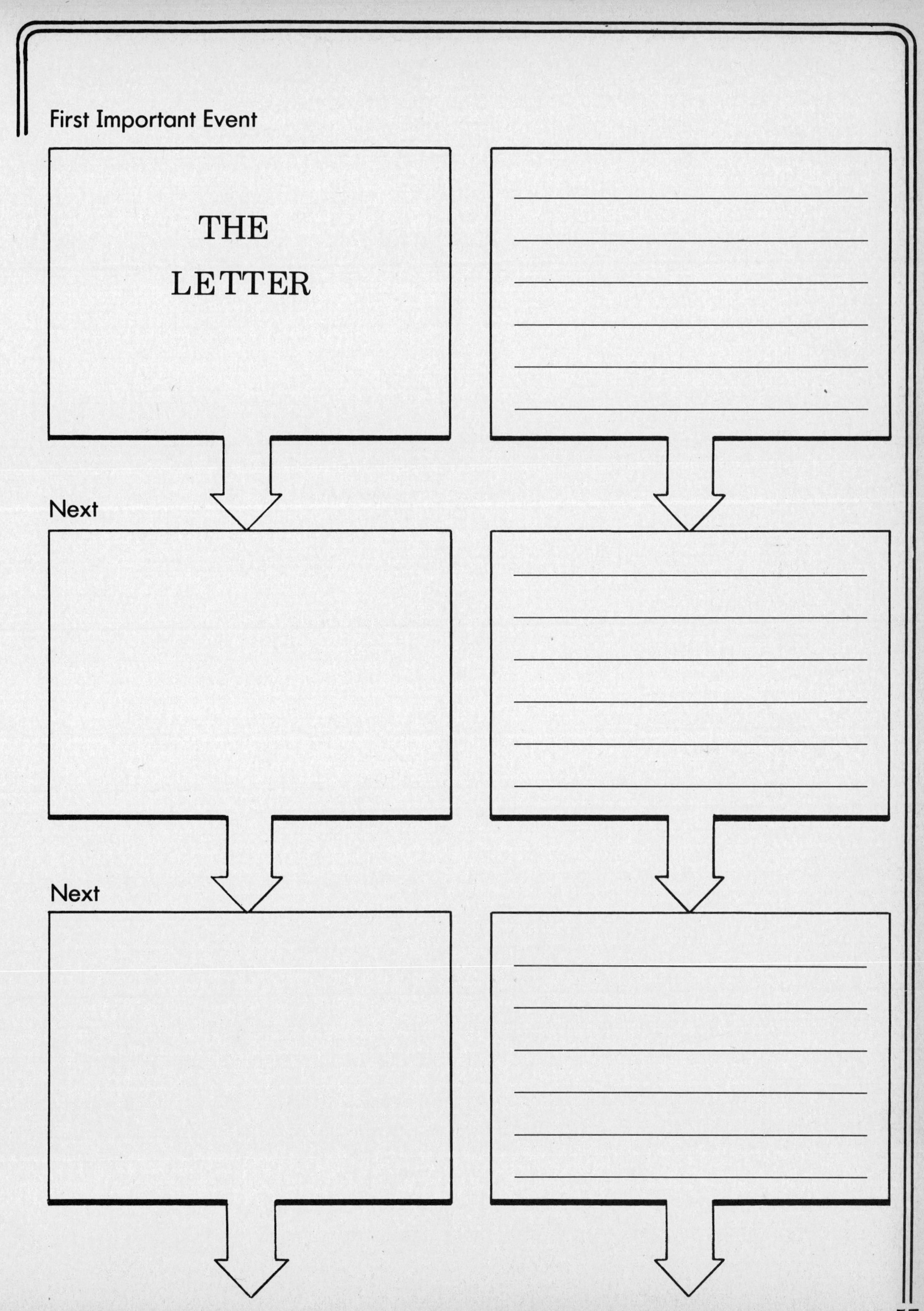
First Important Event
THE
LETTER
Next
Next

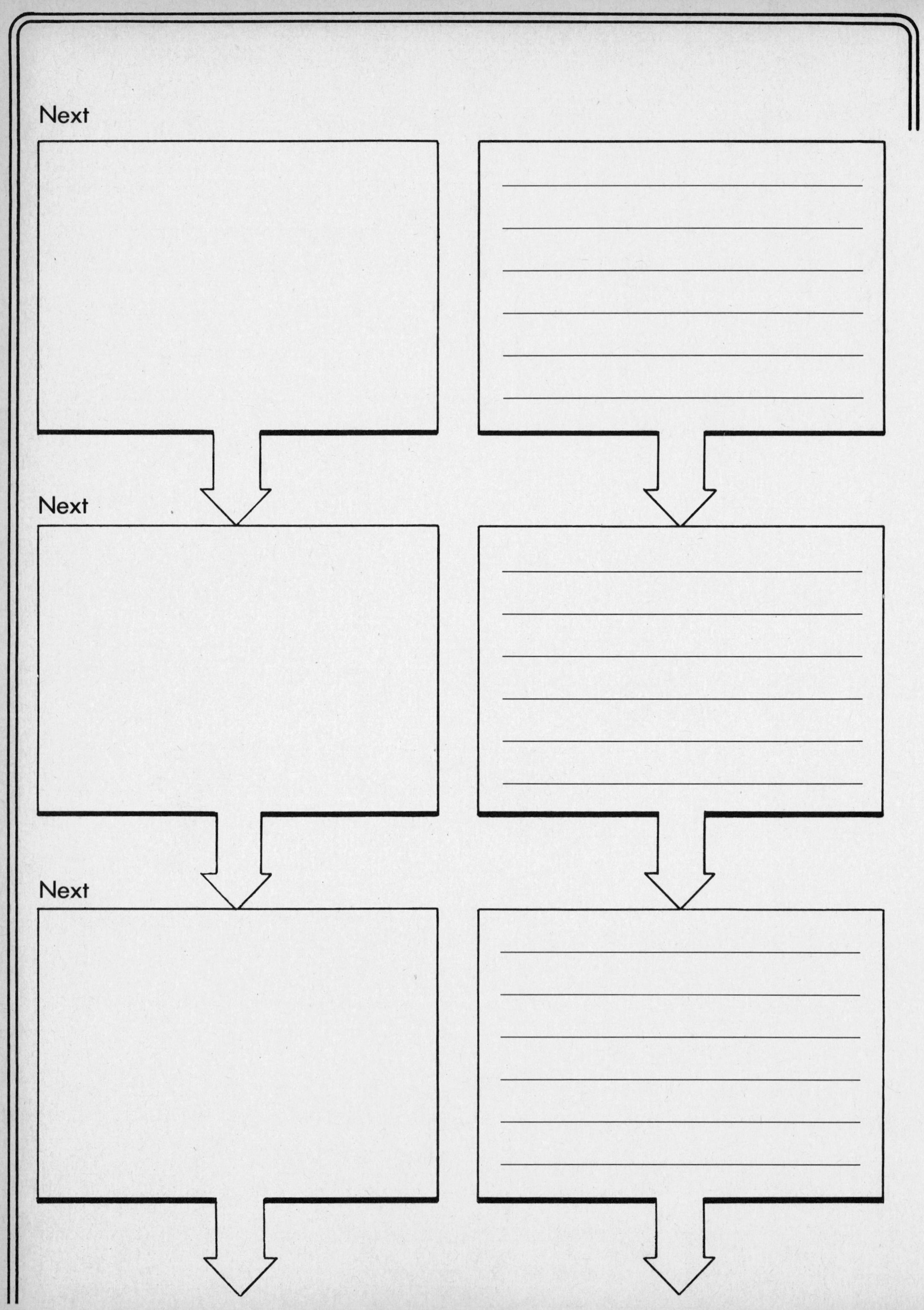
Next
Next
Next

End

Use your map to retell "Dear Aunt Helen" to a partner. Did you leave out any important events? If so, correct your map.

Vocabulary Development

You have learned that the meaning of a new word often can be decided by noticing how it is used in the story.

1. In "Dear Aunt Helen," the author says that Joseph *trudged* home from school.

   What do you think *trudged* means? ______________________________

   ____

   ____

2. Read the words that follow. Draw a circle around the two words that have almost the same meanings.

ran	plodded	skipped
walked	shuffled	crawled

3. The author uses the word *flabbergasted* to describe how Joseph's mother felt about his cooking dinner. What does *flabbergasted* mean? Write your answer on the lines that follow. ____________________

____

____

4. Think of a time when you were *flabbergasted* about something. Write a sentence about it on the lines below. Be sure to use *flabbergasted* in your sentence. ____________________

____

____

5. Authors often use words in unusual ways. You have learned that this is called **figurative language.** In the story the author says that Joseph whipped the egg whites until he thought his *arm would fall off.* Which of the sentences below describes what happened to Joseph's arm? Place a check beside the answer.

____ Joseph's arm was breaking off.

____ Joseph's arm was tired and hurting.

STEP OUT ON YOUR OWN

Writing

In "Dear Aunt Helen" the author doesn't tell you how Joseph's parents feel about his writing to a pen pal. How do you think your parents would feel if you had a pen pal and wrote to him or her often? Write an ending to the story telling what happens when Joseph's parents find out about his pen pal. Use the following space to make some notes before you write. ______________________

Use the following space to begin your rough draft. Continue on another piece of paper.

Share your rough draft with one or more writing partners. Get their ideas for any revisions that can make your writing even better.

Lesson 6: REMEMBERING LAST SUMMER (PART I)

by Sheila Stroup

GET INTO STEP **Prior Knowledge**

1. Read each of the following questions. Answer at least one question on the lines below.

- Do you have a pet that is very special to you? If so, why is it so special?
- Think about your favorite activity to do with a friend. What is it?

2. Make some predictions about "Remembering Last Summer." What do you think the story will be about?

STEP INTO THE STORY **Guided Reading**

Read Part I of "Remembering Last Summer" to find out if any of your predictions are true.

I used to have this terrific old dog named Pepper. He wasn't any particular kind of dog, but he was one of the best friends I ever had. My other really good friend was Bobby Nelson; he lived next door. Every afternoon we'd all sit on my back steps, eating peanut butter on cheese crackers, and Bobby and I would tell each other the dreams we'd had the night before.

Who is the very best friend you've ever had? Was your friend a person or a pet? Write a sentence or two about that friend. ____________________

____

____

____

My grandma liked to sit in her rocker on the back porch and listen to us while she worked on her knitting. Grandma lives at our house. She doesn't look like the grandmothers in books, but she's really a neat person. She spends most of her time reading, taking care of her plants and knitting. I must have a jillion sweaters.

Have you ever known a really neat older person? ____________________
If so, what was it about that person that made him or her so special?

____

____

Anyway, one of my favorite remembering things is those lazy days of sitting on the back steps, sharing dreams and listening to the click-click-click of grandma's knitting needles. One time grandma even told us her dream. She dreamed our house didn't have any doors, and the only way she could get in it was to climb up this gigantic ladder and slide down a wiggly slide that went through the picture window. That's the neat kind of person my grandma is.

Then one day last summer, Bobby called me on the tin-can telephone we'd hooked up between our bedrooms. He yelled, "My father's got a new job. We're moving to Ohio."

That made me very mad at Bobby, even though I knew it wasn't his fault. I kept picturing him telling someone else his dreams or maybe even telling someone my dreams! I don't know why, but it really made me mad.

The day that Bobby moved was awful. First a big van came, and the movers packed up everything except the suitcases and boxes the Nelsons put in their station wagon. When it was time to say good-bye, I gave Bobby my book on insects, which he was always borrowing, and he gave me two of his Indian arrowheads.

What words best describe how the girl in the story is feeling now? Write the words on these lines.

______________________ ______________________

______________________ ______________________

Have you ever felt this way?______________________

After Bobby left, Pepper and I were together all the time. We started spending a lot of time down by the river. Sometimes I'd take my fishing pole and a can of worms, and sometimes we'd just look for turtles and wild flowers.

Pepper even stayed with me when I practiced the piano. He would sit at my feet and make little growly sounds—he never cared too much for the piano—except when I played "The Happy Farmer." Then he'd raise his head high and sing his heart out. He really liked that one, maybe because I had practiced it enough to get rid of most of the mistakes.

Then one terrible night, when we were catching lightning bugs, Pepper let out a cry and fell over. He just lay there shaking and trying to wag his tail a little. I ran and got Daddy, and right away he came back with me and carried Pepper into the house and laid him on his rug. I sat down next to Pepper and petted him and talked to him. He reached out and licked my hand, and then he just closed his eyes. Daddy reached down and felt Pepper's chest, and then he told me Pepper was dead. Daddy said his old heart had just stopped working.

"No, you're wrong!" I shouted. "You're wrong, wrong, wrong!"

Think of a time when you lost someone or something very important to you.

Can you remember how you felt? ______________________________

Do you think the girl in the story feels the same way? ______________________________

____

I don't remember much more about that night, except that later Daddy wrapped Pepper up in his rug and carried him outside. I held the flashlight and knelt on the ground next to Pepper while Daddy dug a hole in the back yard. You know how your mouth feels after the dentist gives you a shot? Well, I felt like that all over, and I couldn't cry. I guess Mom put me to bed, because the next thing I knew, it was morning.

Think carefully about these next questions about Part I of "Remembering Last Summer." Although there are no right or wrong answers, your answers should make sense.

- At the end of Part I, the girl in the story said she couldn't cry when Pepper died. Why do you think she was unable to cry when her pet died?________
- In Part I of the story, the girl loses both of her best friends, Bobby and Pepper. How do you think she felt?

Share your answers with a partner who has also read the story. Talk about why you each answered as you did.

Story Mapping

Can you figure out the most important events in Part I of "Remembering Last Summer"? Use the events to write your story map in the shapes that are drawn. In the boxes on the left, make a drawing or write key words to help you remember the order of events in the story. You might not need all the spaces that are provided. Be sure to include information about the setting.

THE SETTING

Main Characters:

Place:

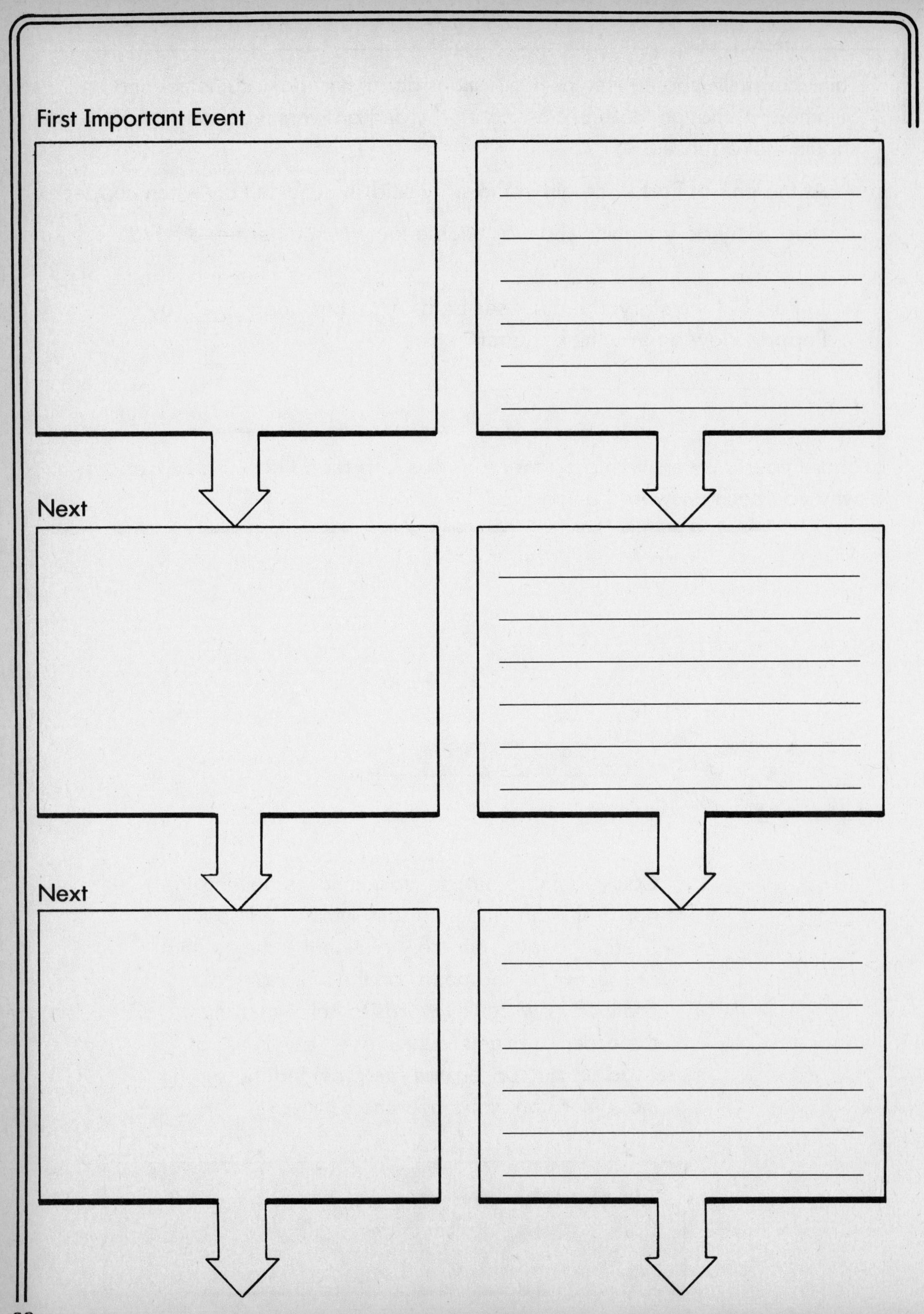

First Important Event
Next
Next

End

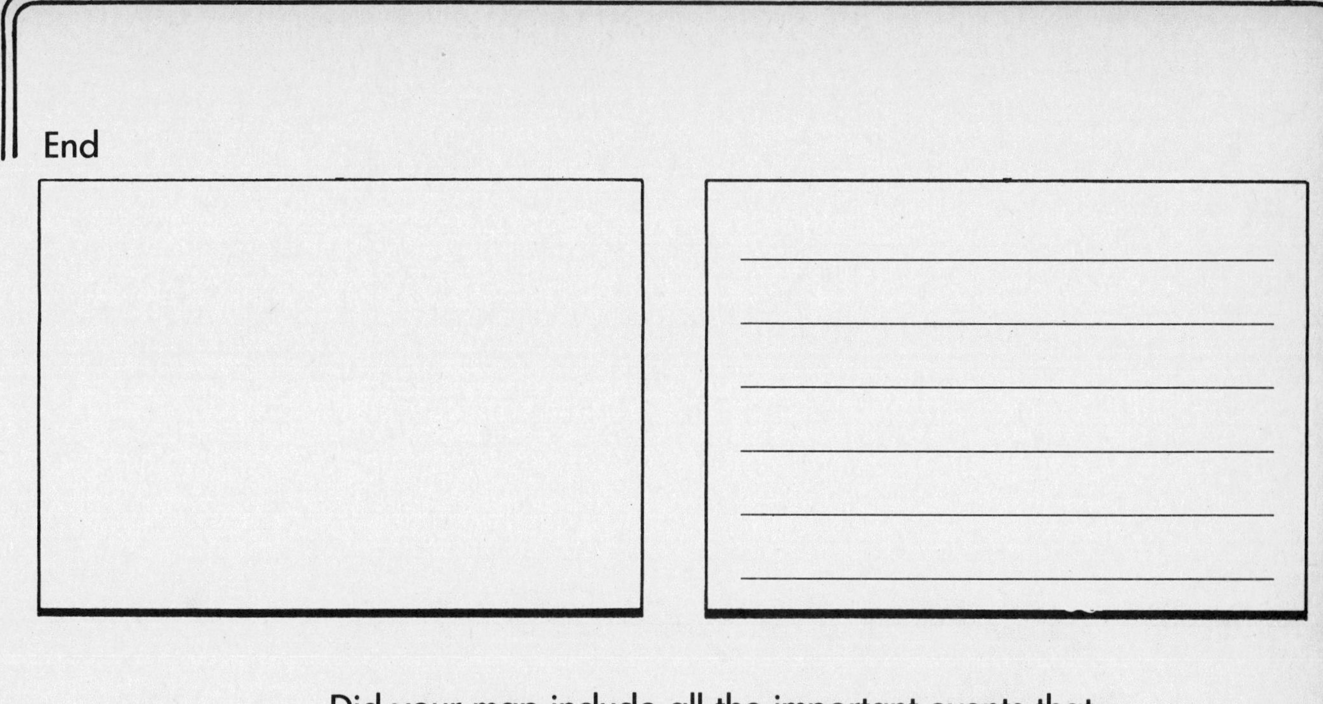

Did your map include all the important events that happened in the first part of the story? Use your map to retell Part I of "Remembering Last Summer" to a partner.

STEP BACK AND THINK **Vocabulary Development**

You have learned that authors often use **figurative language** to help you understand something better. Figurative language helps you to see and feel what is happening in a story.

1. In "Remembering Last Summer," the girl describes how she felt when her dog died, saying:

> "You know how your mouth feels after the dentist gives you a shot? Well, I felt like that all over, and I couldn't cry."

Write some words on the lines that follow, that describe the girl's feelings.

______________________ ______________________

______________________ ______________________

2. Choose one or more of the words you wrote in number 1 and write a new sentence about how the girl felt. Use the lines that follow. ____________

____

____

3. Which description best explains the girl's feelings—yours or the author's? Why? ____

____

____

4. Another use of figurative language occurred when the author described how Pepper liked to sing while the girl played "The Happy Farmer" on the piano. The author says that Pepper *sang his heart out.* Which of the following phrases best describes what the dog did? Place a check beside the answer.

____ Pepper sang until he made himself sick.
____ Pepper sang as loudly and happily as he could.
____ Pepper sang in a sad and whimpering voice.

5. Think about a time when you felt like "singing your heart out." Write a sentence that tells why you felt that way. ____________

____

____

STEP OUT ON YOUR OWN **Writing**

Now that you've read the first part of "Remembering Last Summer," how do you think it will end? How would you like for it to end? You become the author and write the ending. Use the lines that follow to make some notes about the ending you will write. ____

____

____

____

____

____

Choose the idea you like best and write a new ending for the story. Start your rough draft on the lines that follow. Use another piece of paper if you need more space.

____

____

____

____

____

____

____

____

____

____

____

PEPPER

Share the ending with your teacher or a partner. Get their ideas for how you can revise your next draft to make the ending even better.

Lesson 7: REMEMBERING LAST SUMMER (PART II)

by Sheila Stroup

GET INTO STEP **Prior Knowledge**

1. Read each of the following questions very carefully. Answer at least one question on the lines below.

- Has there ever been a time when you felt you didn't have any friends? Tell about it.
- Think of a time when you were really sad. What happened to make you feel better?

____

____

____

____

2. What do you think will happen in Part II of "Remembering Last Summer"? Make some predictions.

____

____

____

____

____

(In Part I of "Remembering Last Summer," the girl who narrates the story told about her two special friends, Bobby and Pepper, her dog. When Bobby moved away, the girl felt very sad and lonely. She began to spend more and more time with Pepper and with her grandmother. Then something terrible happened. Pepper died very suddenly one evening. That night she and her daddy buried

Pepper in the back yard. Pepper's death left her so sad and upset that she couldn't believe what had happened. The whole horrible evening seemed like a bad dream.)

STEP INTO THE STORY **Guided Reading**

Read Part II of "Remembering Last Summer" to find out if any predictions you made about the story are true.

I lay in bed, pretending that the night before had just been the worst dream I'd ever had. Then I got up and tiptoed downstairs. No one else was awake yet. When I walked into the kitchen, Pepper's rug was gone; and when I went out to the back yard, there was the mound of lumpy dirt. I knew I couldn't pretend any more. I sat down on the back porch steps and wished that Bobby still lived next door. I felt terrible.

Think of a time when you felt the way the girl is feeling now. Write a sentence about it. ______________________________

____

____

Pretty soon I heard noises in the kitchen. Mom was up making coffee. I guess she knew how I felt, because for once she didn't make me eat breakfast. A little while later, grandma came out and sat in her rocking chair.

I said, "Grandma, promise you'll never leave me."

"Oh, I can't promise that," she said. "Someday, I'll have to leave you, just as Pepper did. Try not to be mad at me."

"I'd never be mad at you!" I told her.

"Oh, you just might," she said. "When Grandpa died, I got very angry at him."

"Why, Grandma?" I asked.

"For leaving me all alone. But I realized that Grandpa didn't want to leave me, and then I felt very sad."

"I'm so sad I don't think anything will be fun ever again," I said.

Have you ever felt like the girl is feeling now? ______________________

If so, what caused you to feel that way? ______________________

____

What made you feel better? ______________________

____

"Did you ever stop feeling sad for Grandpa?"

"Yes, yes." She nodded. "I still miss Grandpa—I always will—but Grandpa didn't like me to be sad. He liked to see me laugh. 'Katherine,' he'd say, 'I love the way you crinkle up your nose when you laugh.' " And she laughed softly, remembering Grandpa.

I was starting to feel a little better. We didn't say anything for awhile. I thought about what she had said and about how Pepper had hated for me to be sad. He would always try to cheer me up by licking me in the face or by bringing me some dumb toy to play with.

Do you have a friend who tries to cheer you up when you're sad? ____________

If so, what does your friend do? ______________________________

____

Later that morning, Grandma and I took a walk down by the river. During our walk, Grandma discovered a tiny tree growing among the flowers. She told me to run home and get her gardening shovel. When I got back, we dug up the tree, being careful not to cut off the roots. I carried it home, and we planted it right in the lumps that Pepper was buried under. Then we watered it with Grandma's sprinkling can. Grandma said that in the spring, when our tree bloomed, we'd always remember Pepper. In a way he'd become a part of the tree.

Do you think Grandma's idea is a good one? Explain your answer. ______

______

______

The rest of that afternoon, Grandma and I sat on the back porch steps and ate peanut butter on cheese crackers and talked. I bet she told me a hundred stories I'd never had time to listen to before.

That day I spent with Grandma after Pepper died was August twenty-first of last summer. And now it's spring already.

Today when I walked home from school, Grandma was watching for me at the picture window. "Come with me!" she said, as she came running out to meet me. "I could hardly wait for you to get here."

What do you think Grandma is so excited about? Make a prediction. ______

______

Read on to find out if you're correct.

I followed her out to the backyard, and she headed straight for our little tree. It had ten cottony white blossoms on it.

"Oh, the flowers are so pretty!" I said. "What kind of a tree is it?"

Grandma's nose got all crinkly. "Why, it's a dogwood tree, of course!" she said. Then we laughed, and I gave her a big hug. Grandma is one of the most terrific friends I've ever had.

The next questions don't have answers that are right or wrong. However, the answers should make sense.

- Do you think that the girl in the story still misses Pepper? Explain your answer.

  ____

  ____

- After you read Part I of "Remembering Last Summer," you wrote a new ending. Which ending did you like best, yours or the real ending? Explain your answer.

  ____

  ____

Share your answers with a partner who has also read "Remembering Last Summer." Tell each other the parts of the story you liked best.

STAY IN STEP **Story Mapping**

What are the most important events in the second part of "Remembering Last Summer"? In the boxes on the left, make a drawing or write key words to help you remember the order of the events in the story. Think about these events and write a story map in the shapes provided. You may not always need all the spaces that are provided. Remember to include information about the setting.

THE SETTING

Main Characters:

Place:

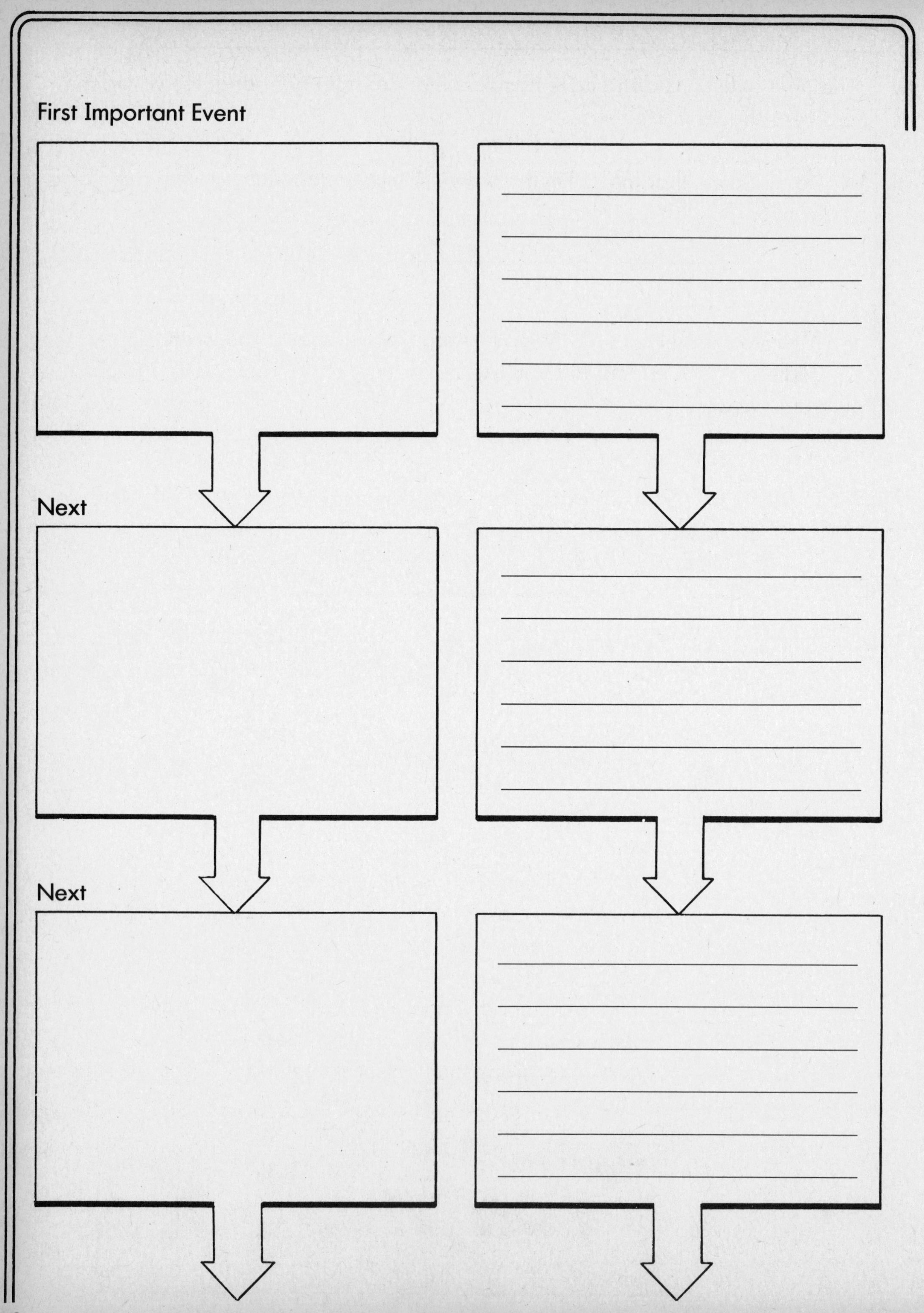
First Important Event
Next
Next

End

Share your map with a partner who has also mapped the second part of "Remembering Last Summer." Did the maps help you and your partner retell the important events in the story? If so, both maps are correct, even if they are different.

QUIET! SUPERMIND AT WORK!

STEP BACK AND THINK Vocabulary Development

Several words in "Remembering Last Summer" have more than one meaning. These words can be used as a **verb** (to show action) or as a **noun** (to name something). On the lines below, write two sentences for each of the words from the story. In the first sentence, use the word as a verb. In the second sentence, use it as a noun. The first two have been done for you.

- rock (Verb) **Mother will rock the baby to help her go to sleep.**
- rock (Noun) **The boy threw a rock and broke the window.**

1. play (Verb) __________

2. play (Noun) __________

3. walk (Verb) __________

4. walk (Noun) ______________________________

____

5. plant (Verb) ______________________________

____

6. plant (Noun) ______________________________

____

7. "Remembering Last Summer" is a story that describes many feelings and emotions. Good authors choose their words carefully so that readers can understand the characters' feelings. Find words from the following list that fit into the categories "happy" and "sad." You may write each word once, more than once or not at all.

cheerful	softly	cry	dark
quiet	twinkle	angry	deserted
laughing	surprise	miserable	beaming
dreary	peaceful	shadows	breathless

a. happy ______________________________

____

____

b. sad ______________________________

____

____

Do you see another group of words in the list? What feeling do these words describe? Use the lines that follow to write the name of the new category and the words that fit into it.

c. ______________________________

____

____

STEP OUT ON YOUR OWN **Writing**

In "Remembering Last Summer," the narrator lost her dog, Pepper. Pepper was her very special friend. The story never mentions whether she gets another dog or not. Do you think she should get a new dog? Write some reasons *for* and *against* getting a new dog. Use the lines that follow.

Reasons FOR a new dog	**Reasons AGAINST a new dog**

Decide which set of reasons you agree with most. Then write a persuasive paragraph to support your opinion. Begin your rough draft in the space below. Use another piece of paper if you need more room.

Ask your teacher or a writing partner to go over your rough draft with you. Ask them for suggestions to make the next draft even more persuasive.

Lesson 8: THE HORRIBLE HUDSONS

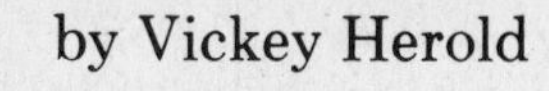

by Vickey Herold

GET INTO STEP **Prior Knowledge**

1. Think about each of the questions that follow. Answer at least one question on the lines below.

- Have you ever promised to do something and then wished you hadn't? Tell about it.
- Have you ever done any babysitting? If so, did anything funny or bad happen?
- Think of a time when someone told you a good story. Write a sentence or two that tells what the story was about and why you liked it.

____

____

____

____

____

2. What do you think "The Horrible Hudsons" will be about? Make some predictions.

____

____

____

____

____

STEP INTO THE STORY **Guided Reading**

Read "The Horrible Hudsons" to find out if any of your predictions are true. As you read, think about what you would do if the things in the story were happening to you.

"Jenny, Dear," Mother said in an almost pleading voice, "you'd better stop just pushing your food across your plate and finish your supper. You're supposed to be at the Hudsons' by 7:30."

"I know, Mom," Jenny answered. "I'm just not very hungry, I guess."

But Jenny knew that wasn't why her supper didn't interest her. It was that she just couldn't eat with the thought of the Horrible Hudsons on her mind. Just thinking of another evening babysitting with them was enough to kill anyone's appetite.

Think of a time when you dreaded something so much that you couldn't even eat. Write a sentence about it. ________________________________

____

____

"Sometimes," thought Jenny, "no amount of money is enough to make some ordeals worthwhile."

Still, the Hudsons did pay three times the amount of money that any of the other parents in the neighborhood paid. Of course, the Hudsons really didn't have much choice. Their twin sons were notorious for their terrible behavior. They were known by the whole neighborhood as the Horrible Hudsons, and no one would sit with them more than once. If Jenny hadn't really needed money for the upcoming weekend ski trip with her friends, she would have never agreed to sit for the twins, either. They were absolute monsters!

Have you ever agreed to do a job to earn money for something special? ____

What was your job? ____________________

____

____

Jenny picked up the book of mystery stories she was reading and headed for the door.

"Good luck, Dear," her mother called after her. "And don't try to read until you're sure they're asleep. It just isn't safe not to watch those two every minute!"

"O.K.," Jenny answered as she closed the door behind her.

The Hudsons' home was only four houses down from her own. It didn't take Jenny long to turn up the walk that led to the Hudsons' front door. When she was about halfway there, the door swung open suddenly and the twins, Justin and Jason, ran out shrieking and shouting with their dad frantically chasing them.

"Jenny," he said, "could you go after Justin while I get Jason? I'm afraid I let them get away from me."

Have you ever known a child who behaved like Justin and Jason? ____

If so, write a sentence or two about that child. ____________________

____

A few minutes later, Mr. Hudson was leading Jason kicking and screaming, back through the front door. Just behind him came Jenny with a firm hold on the back of Justin's pajamas.

"Now, boys," said Mr. Hudson trying to use his sternest possible voice, "you behave while your mother and I are out. Don't give Jenny any trouble."

Then he flashed Jenny a quick smile and shrugged as if to say, "I've done all I can do. You're on your own."

Almost immediately Mrs. Hudson came down the stairs. She already had on her coat and was carrying her handbag.

"I've left the number where we'll be," she told her. "The boys are all ready for bed, if you can get them to go. Just do your best, Jenny. I know they can be difficult sometimes."

"Yes," agreed Mr. Hudson. "Just try not to let them do any damage, like breaking something."

"Or leaving the water running," said Mrs. Hudson.

"Or flushing washcloths down the toilet."

"Or putting the cat in the dishwasher."

"I'll try," promised Jenny. But she couldn't manage to sound too sure.

Would you babysit with the Horrible Hudsons? ____________

Tell why or why not. ____________

____

As Jenny watched the Hudsons walk quickly toward their car, she couldn't help thinking that they looked like they were running away. She had an overwhelming desire to escape, too.

Just then, Jason pushed her hard from behind. "We don't have to do what you say. We don't have to do anything we don't want to!"

"Yeah," added Justin. "We always do whatever we want."

What would you do if this were happening to you? ____________

____

Do you think Jenny will do the same thing? ____________

The battle lines were drawn. Jenny took a deep breath and in a strict voice said, "All right, you two, let's all go up to your room and have a nice game of Bingo or Chutes and Ladders. And if you're real good, I'll read you a bedtime story when we've finished."

"Forget it," they shouted at once. "Those are baby things and we're not babies!"

"Then why do you need a babysitter?" asked Jenny.

The boys had to have some time to think.

They hadn't expected that question.

"Because," answered Jason after a minute, "we get into trouble if we're left alone."

"Then that proves you're babies, doesn't it?" Jenny said in a matter of fact voice. "Only babies get into trouble when they're left alone. Big boys can stay by themselves without causing any trouble."

Do you think that what Jenny said will make the twins behave? Make a prediction about what she will do. ______________________________

____

"We'll be big boys then and not cause trouble," Justin said. "Then we won't have to go to bed. Big boys can stay up as late as they want."

"Yeah," added Jason. "Big boys can stay up all night if they want to, and that's what we're going to do."

Quick as a flash, both boys ran into the living room. Jason jumped onto one sofa while his brother jumped onto the chair across from it. At first they used the furniture like trampolines, each trying to jump higher than the other.

"Stop that," shouted Jenny. "You're acting just like babies, not like big boys."

"We're not babies!" Justin yelled back. "We're soldiers parachuting over enemy territory. I'm going to land right on my target!"

With that announcement, he gave one big push off of the cushion, and shot straight up into the air When he came down, he landed right on top of the cat who was unlucky enough to be walking by at just the wrong moment. The poor, startled animal hissed loudly and struggled to get away from her attacker. As they rolled across the floor, they hit the table beside the chair. The lamp fell with a big crash!

What do you think will happen next? Make some predictions. ______

______

______

"All right," said Jenny in a voice that really showed her anger, "that's enough!"

"Both of you get into bed," she ordered. Jason and Justin each climbed into their beds as Jenny stood between them.

"But we don't want to go to bed," Justin whined. "We're not sleepy."

"I'll read you a story, then," answered Jenny as she walked over to the little bookcase that stood in the corner of the room.

"We don't want you to read us one of those baby stories. Tell us a good one instead," Justin pleaded. "We'll listen to a good story."

Jenny searched her mind for a story she could tell. Then she remembered the book of mystery stories she had been reading.

"How about a mystery story with robbers and detectives in it? Or one that has ghosts and pirate treasure?"

"Yeah!" the twins agreed excitedly. "Tell both of them!"

Jenny walked over to the doorway and turned off the light. Only the light from the hallway lit the room. "O.K." she said. "But mystery stories are better in the dark."

She returned to the boys' beds and sat down on the floor between them. She told them the story of the queen's missing emeralds. To her surprise, the boys were actually listening. When she finished the story, they demanded another. So she told them the one about the pirate's ghost and the vanishing chest of Spanish treasure.

The boys listened and listened. Shortly before nine o'clock, their eyes began to grow heavy. They sank back a little farther into their pillows and pulled the covers up to their chins. Soon they were sleeping soundly.

Jenny tiptoed out of the boys' room and went back downstairs. She picked up the lamp and straightened the cushions on the furniture. Then she picked up her book of mysteries and opened it to the next story.

"Only 9:10," she thought to herself. "The Hudsons won't be back for hours. This is going to be a snap!"

Think carefully about each of the questions below. Even though there are no right or wrong answers, your answers should make sense.

- Do you think that the Hudson twins are really horrible? Explain your answer.

  ____

  ____

- Do you think that Jenny will agree to babysit for the Hudsons again?

  ____

  ____

- Do you think that Jenny should tell the Hudsons about how well the twins liked the exciting mystery stories?

  ____

  Explain your answer.

  ____

  ____

Share your answers with a partner who also read this story. Tell each other about your favorite parts.

Story Mapping

Think about what you read and about the important events in "The Horrible Hudsons." In the boxes on the left, make a drawing or write key words to help you remember the order of the events in the story. Use the events to write a story map in the shapes that are provided. Remember, you may not always need all the spaces that are provided. Be sure to include information about the setting.

THE SETTING

Main Characters:

Place:

First Important Event

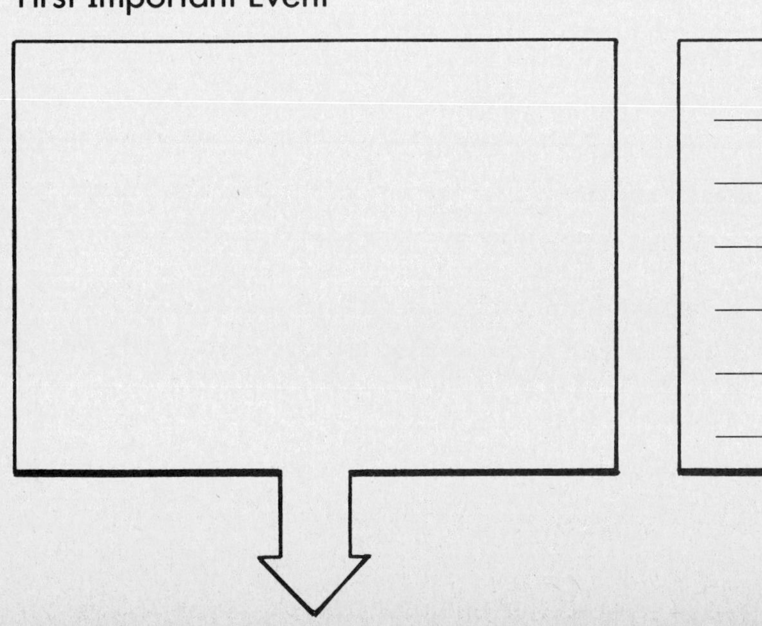

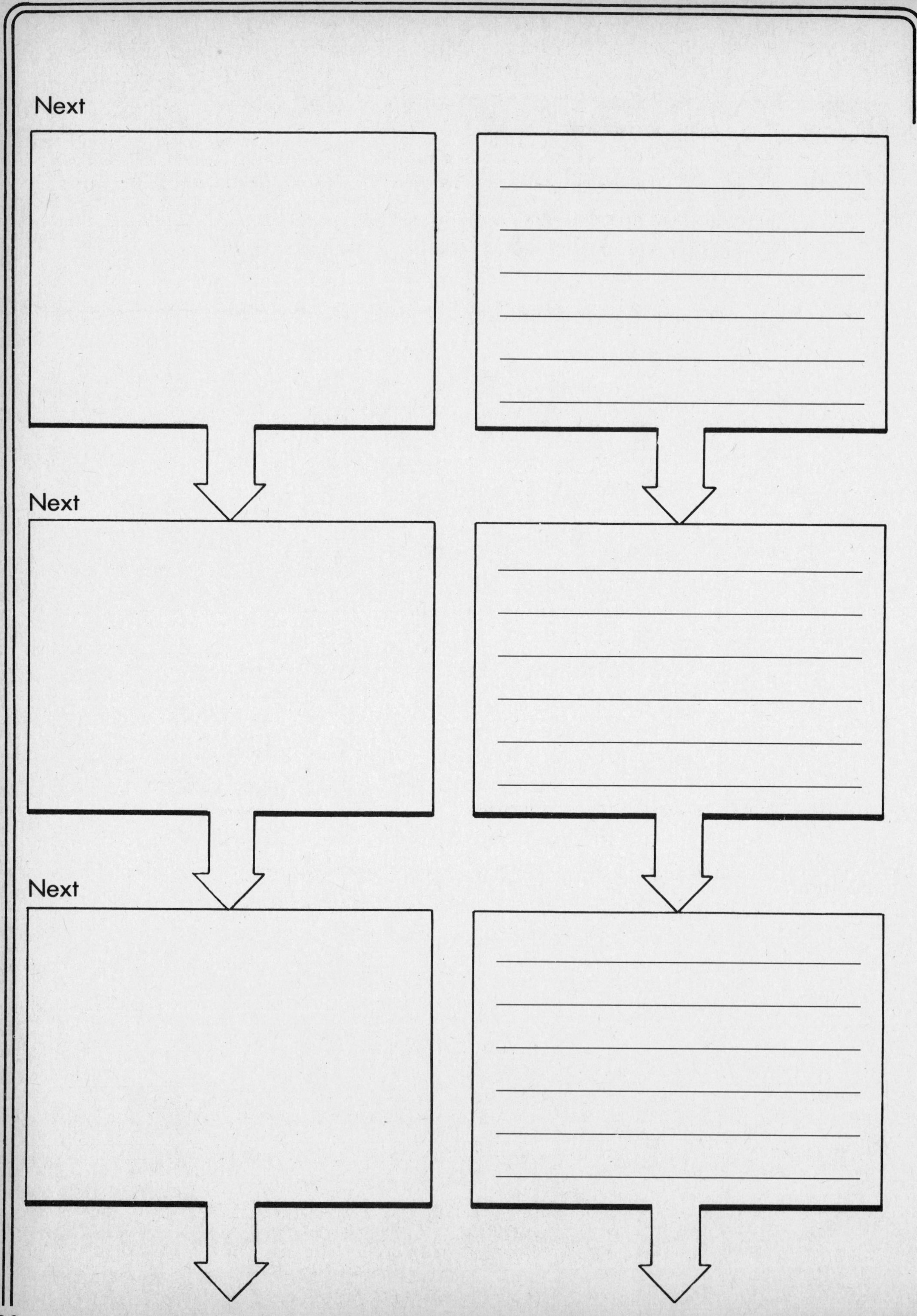
Next
Next
Next

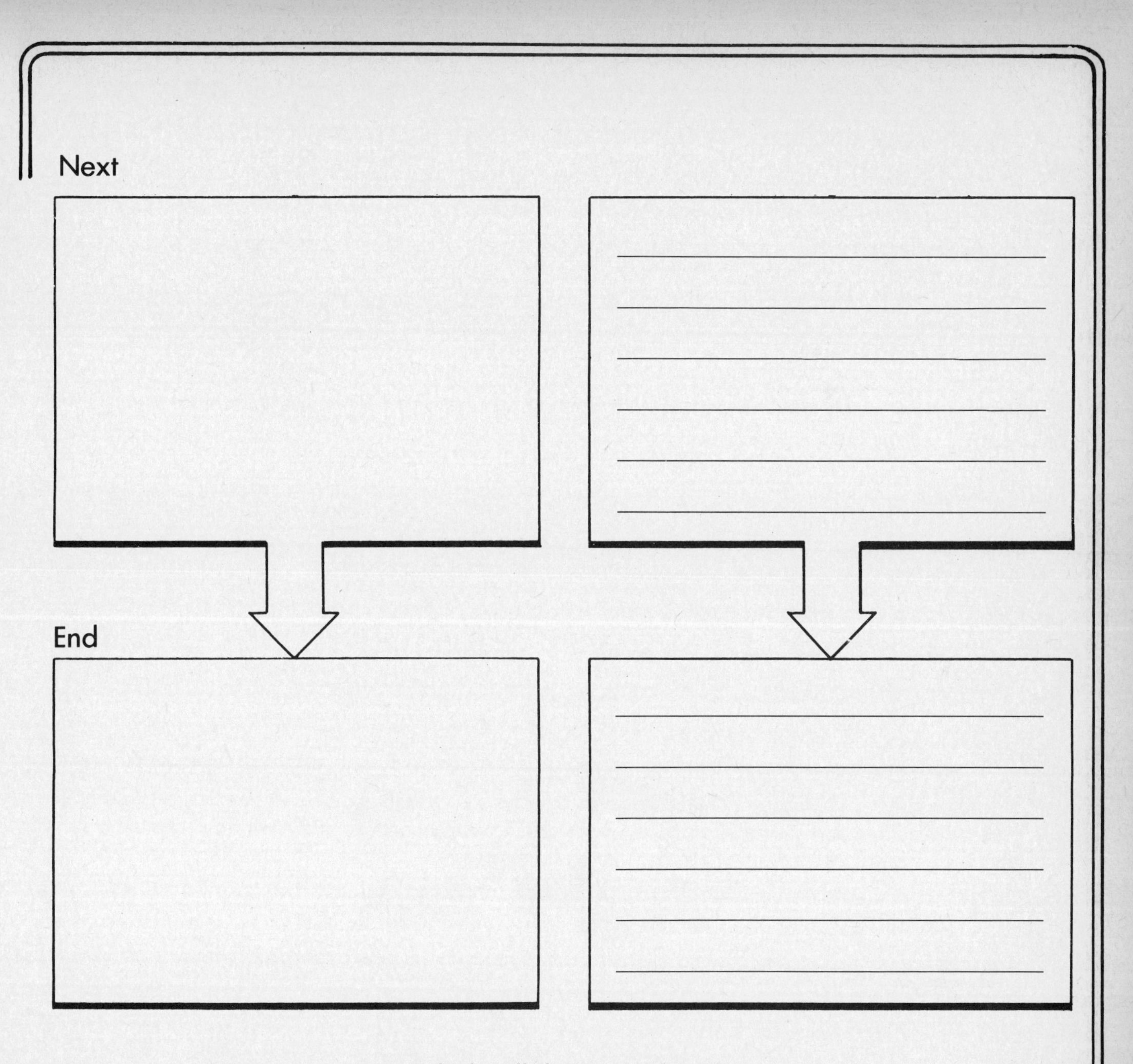

Does your map include all the important events that happened in the story? Use your map to retell "The Horrible Hudsons."

STEP BACK AND THINK Vocabulary Development

You know that writers often use colorful words to explain their feelings about something. Some words suggest a pleasant meaning and others suggest an unpleasant meaning. You have learned that these meanings are called **connotations.**

Read the following sets of sentences. Decide whether each sentence has a pleasant or an unpleasant connotation. Write most pleasant or most unpleasant on the lines that follow.

1. The Hudson twins were horrible. ______________________
2. The Hudson twins were naughty. ______________________

3. We get into mischief if we're left alone. ______________________
4. We get into trouble if we're left alone. ______________________

5. The animal was startled. ______________________
6. The animal was terrified. ______________________

You know that a **simile** makes a comparison by using "like" or "as." A **metaphor** makes a comparison without using "like" or "as." In a metaphor a person or thing is said to *be* something else. For example:

The candidate's speech was dynamite.

What two things are being compared? How are they alike?

The author of "The Horrible Hudsons" used metaphors to describe several incidents in the story. Read the following examples. Then answer the questions.

7. At the beginning of the story, Jenny said the twins were absolute monsters.

   What two things are being compared? ______________________________

   How are they alike? ______________________________

   ____

   ____

8. When the twins were jumping on the furniture, they said they were soldiers parachuting over enemy territory.

   What two things are being compared? ______________________________

   How are they alike? ______________________________

   ____

STEP OUT ON YOUR OWN — Writing

Jenny controlled the Horrible Hudsons by telling them exciting stories until they went to sleep. What if you had been sitting with the twins? What might you have done to keep the boys entertained and out of trouble? List some ideas on the following lines.

Choose the ideas you think are best and write a story about what you would do if you were babysitting the Horrible Hudsons. Use the lines that follow to write your rough draft. Continue on another piece of paper if you need more space.

I'M BABYSITTING TONIGHT!

Read your rough draft. Does it make sense? Do you need to make any changes? Share it with a partner. Get ideas for revisions that can make your story better when you rewrite.

Lesson 9: MOM SLEEPS IN

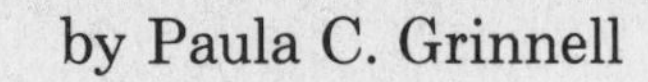

by Paula C. Grinnell

GET INTO STEP | Prior Knowledge

BOING

1. Read the following questions carefully. Answer at least one question on the lines below.

- Have you ever had a morning when absolutely everything went wrong? Tell what happened.
- Think about a time when you thought no one appreciated you. How did it make you feel? Did you do anything about it?

____

____

____

____

2. What do you think "Mom Sleeps In" will be about? Write some predictions.

____

____

____

____

STEP INTO THE STORY **Guided Reading**

Read "Mom Sleeps In" to find out if any of your predictions are true.

The radio went on at 6:45 a.m., just like it did every morning. Laura moaned and rolled over. "It can't be morning yet," she groaned. "Oh, well. At least I have a few more minutes before Mom comes in to drag me out of bed. I'll just listen to my favorite disc jockey."

Suddenly, Laura was jolted out of bed with the words, "News flash: All Mothers Are On Strike Today! After years of working without pay and without recognition, the mothers in our town are angry. They've decided to let the men and children see just how hard moms work by letting them do the housework and chores that mothers usually do. Well folks, it's going to be an interesting day!"

What would you think if you heard this news flash? ______________________

____

After getting over her initial alarm, Laura decided that her mother was above such things. Certainly her mother wouldn't go on strike. And besides, she appreciated her mother. Why, every Mother's Day she made breakfast in bed for her mom and gave her a little present. Well, maybe she didn't always help when Mom asked; but gosh, she was only eleven. What would you expect?

Laura emerged from her thoughts long enough to realize that it was 7:05. Mom hadn't come in to wake her up at 7:00 like she always did. Laura began to panic, but she quickly got control of herself. "Oh, Mom just overslept, or maybe the baby is sick. I'm sure there's a simple explanation. Mom wouldn't desert us!"

Just to make sure, however, Laura decided that she had better search the house for her mother. There was no sense checking the shower. She could hear her father singing in there. She began in the baby's room. There was no sign of Mom. She went on to her brother's room, the kitchen, the living room and finally discovered her mother still in bed, sound asleep. "She just forgot to set her alarm," she thought. "I'd better wake her up."

Do you think Laura's mother has overslept, or is she taking part in the strike?

Write your prediction. ______________________________

____

Read on to find out if you're right.

Laura shook her mom. "Mom, Mom, get up. We'll be late for school."

"I just thought I'd rest some this morning," replied Mom. "I've been working too hard lately. I need a day off. You shouldn't have any trouble getting yourself ready. You're a big girl, now."

"But what about Josh? And what do I do if the baby wakes up?" Laura's voice became more like a whine as she became convinced that her mother was taking part in the strike.

"You can handle it. I must go back to sleep now. Have a good day. See you when you get home."

It was clear that Laura was going to get nowhere with her mom. She decided there was no more time to waste. It was up to Laura, the oldest, to take over.

What do you suppose Laura is thinking about this situation? ______________________

____

____

____

Would you think the same thing? ______________________

She dashed into Josh's room. To her surprise, he was already dressed. She was really pleased. "Hey, this is going to be a snap," she thought. Then the full picture came into view. Josh's pajama top was poking up out of his bright red plaid shirt which had been matched to his maroon sweat pants. As if that wasn't bad enough, he had chosen green socks which he wore over his sweat pants. This "outfit" was topped off with his treasured pair of soccer shoes complete with a pile of mud from the last game. Now that Laura's eyes were on the floor, she noticed that the dry mud was in danger of going back to its original wetness because the water from the bathroom sink was still running. It was competing for floor space with the trail of toothpaste that went from the bathroom sink to Josh's dresser and back again. In fact, the toys scattered all over the floor were about to be swept away. As Laura was considering the joy she would feel over this last possibility, she came to her senses and jumped into action.

She turned the water off, scooped up two towels, threw one to Josh, and started mopping up with the other. He didn't need to be told what to do. The expression on her face was enough to convince him that he had better help without any discussion.

Intimidation didn't last long with Josh, however. Besides, cleaning up wasn't much fun, and Josh was on the lookout for a good excuse to drop his towel and move on. The baby gave him that excuse when she woke up and shouted, "Mama."

Before Laura could open her mouth, Josh had set a new record on the race course between his room and Sarah's. "Hi, Beebee!" Josh exclaimed, using his favorite term for the baby. "Want to come out and play?" he asked, as he pulled down the side of the crib and grabbed her. As Sarah struggled to get loose, he prevailed and plopped her on the floor. Feeling solid ground, Sarah ran for the protection of her sister.

Now what do you think will happen? Write a prediction. ____________________

____

____

Laura was wondering if she would ever get to school when she looked up and saw Sarah using the bathroom floor like a skating rink. She held out her arms just in time to catch Sarah and prevent another disaster. As she felt Sarah's wet body slam into her, Laura decided that it was time to get Dad,

"Josh," Laura yelled with her voice just a notch below hysterical, "Go get Dad. Tell him we need his help. This is an emergency!"

When Josh reached the hall, he used his playground voice to notify his father of the importance of the situation, "Daaaaaad. Come quick!"

What will Dad do when he sees what has happened? Do you think he knows about the strike? ______________________________

____

____

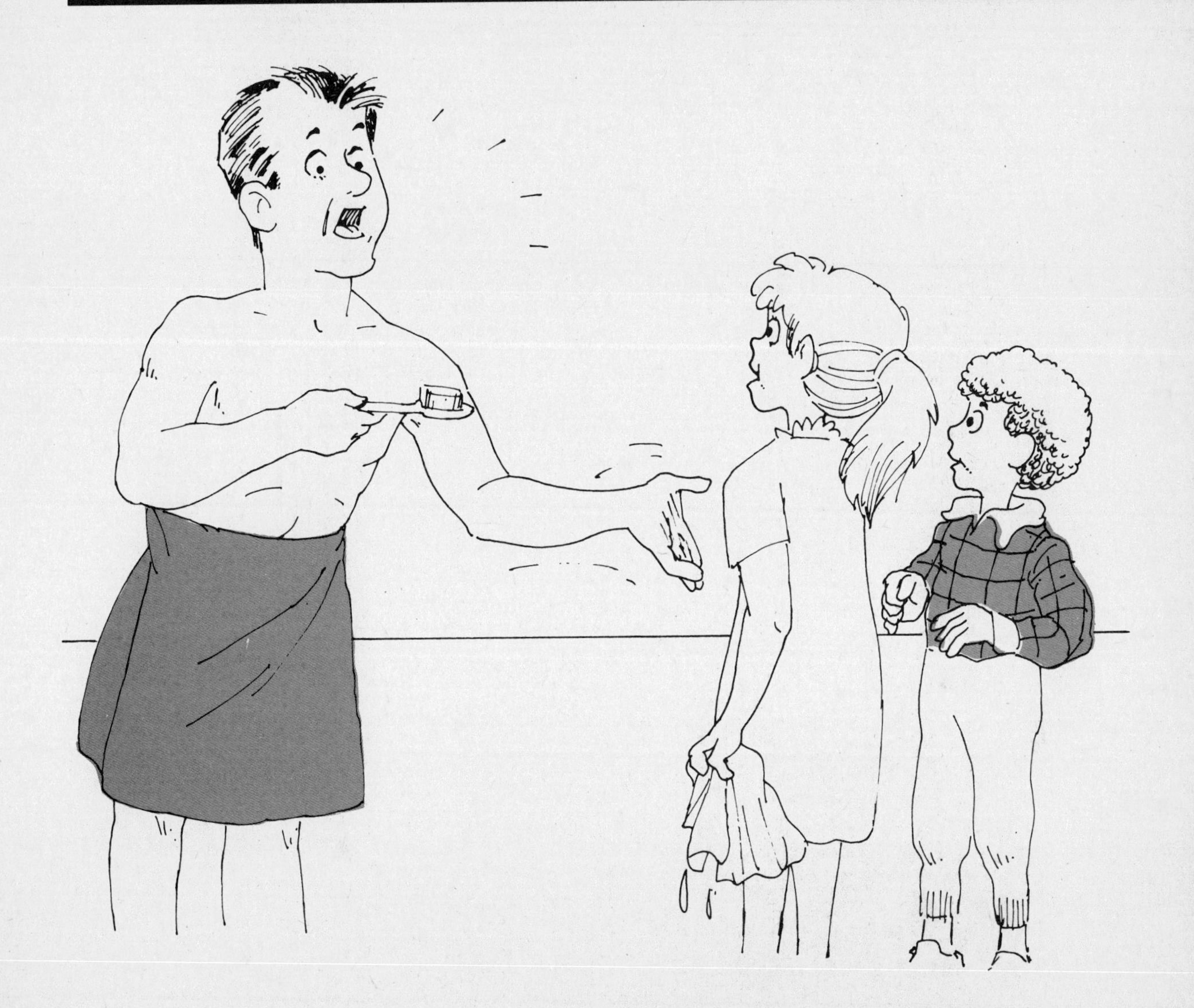

Dad barely had time to wrap a towel around himself as he flew toward the sound of Josh's voice. Questions began pouring out of Dad's mouth as quickly as the water had poured out of the sink. "What happened? Why aren't you dressed for school yet, Laura? And, for goodness sake, *who* dressed Josh?!" With his voice slowly rising, Dad finally got to the big question: "Where is your mother?!"

Now how was Laura going to answer that one, she wondered. After sorting through a number of possibilities, Laura decided upon the truth as the most sensible response this time. She began with the "News flash" on the radio and spared no details in replaying the morning's events.

"Well kids, it certainly has been an eventful morning! It sounds to me like it's time to negotiate some end of strike terms with your mother. What do you think?" asked Dad.

"Yes!" the answer came back in unison, with the baby repeating it just to be part of the action.

"That sounds good to me, too!" Mother chimed in. After seeing this room, I'm ready to negotiate, too! We can start by deciding who's going to clean up this mess!"

That broke the ice. They had a five person hug and a good laugh before they all pitched in to help. All except the baby that is, who continued to mess up as everyone else cleaned!

Give some careful thought to each of these next questions. Although there are no right or wrong answers, your answers should make sense.

- Do you think that Laura's mother was right to join that strike? _____ Explain your answer. ______________________________

  ____

- The author doesn't tell whether the experiences that Laura's family had made them appreciate Mom more. What do you think? Explain your answer. ______________________________

  ____

  ____

Share your answers with a partner who has also read "Mom Sleeps In." Talk about how they are alike and how they are different.

Story Mapping

What are the main events in "Mom Sleeps In"? In the boxes on the left, make a drawing or write key words to help you remember the order of the events in the story. Think about these events and write a story map in the shapes that are provided. You may not need to use all the spaces. Be sure to include important information about the setting.

THE SETTING

Main Characters:

Place:

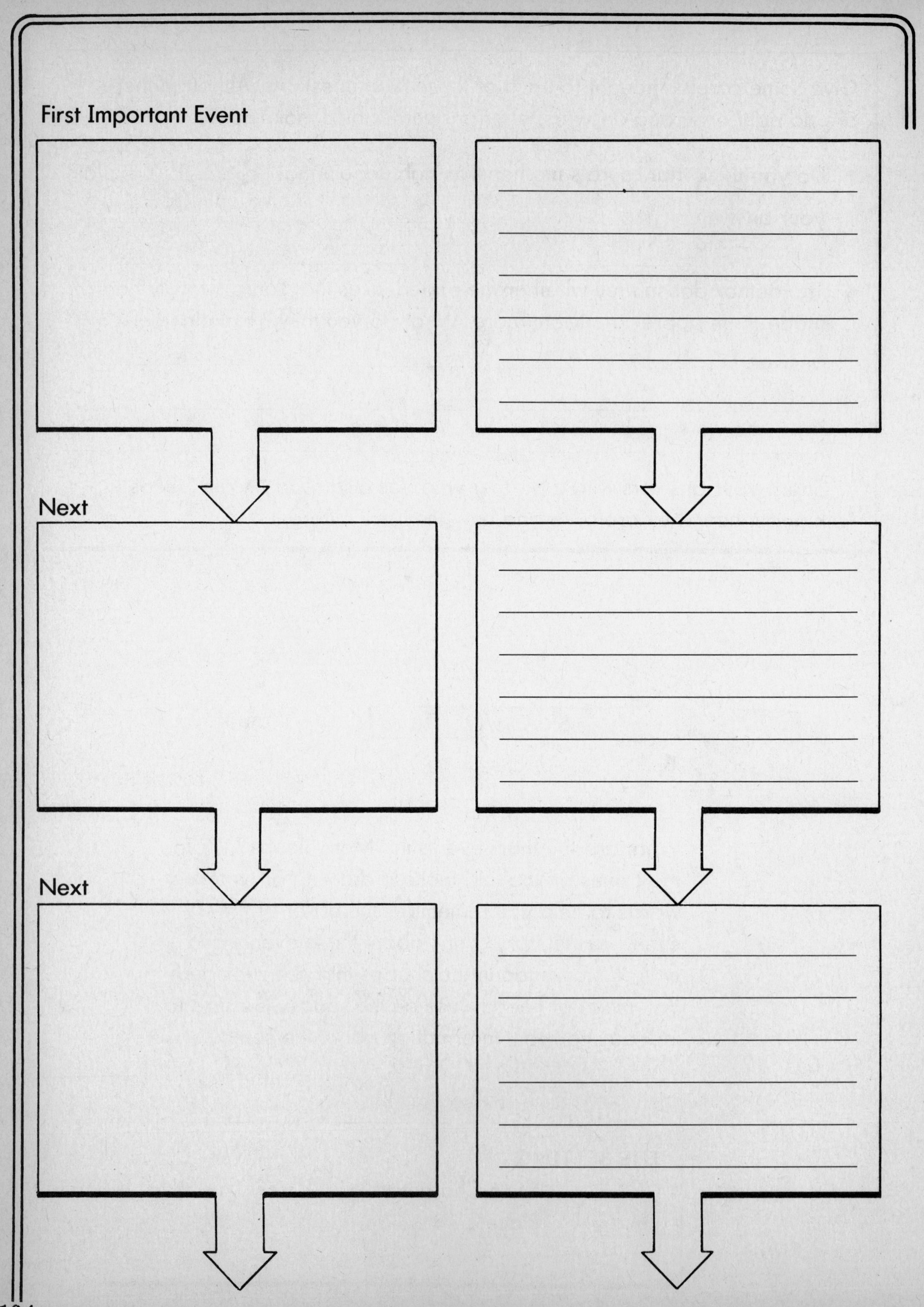
First Important Event
Next
Next

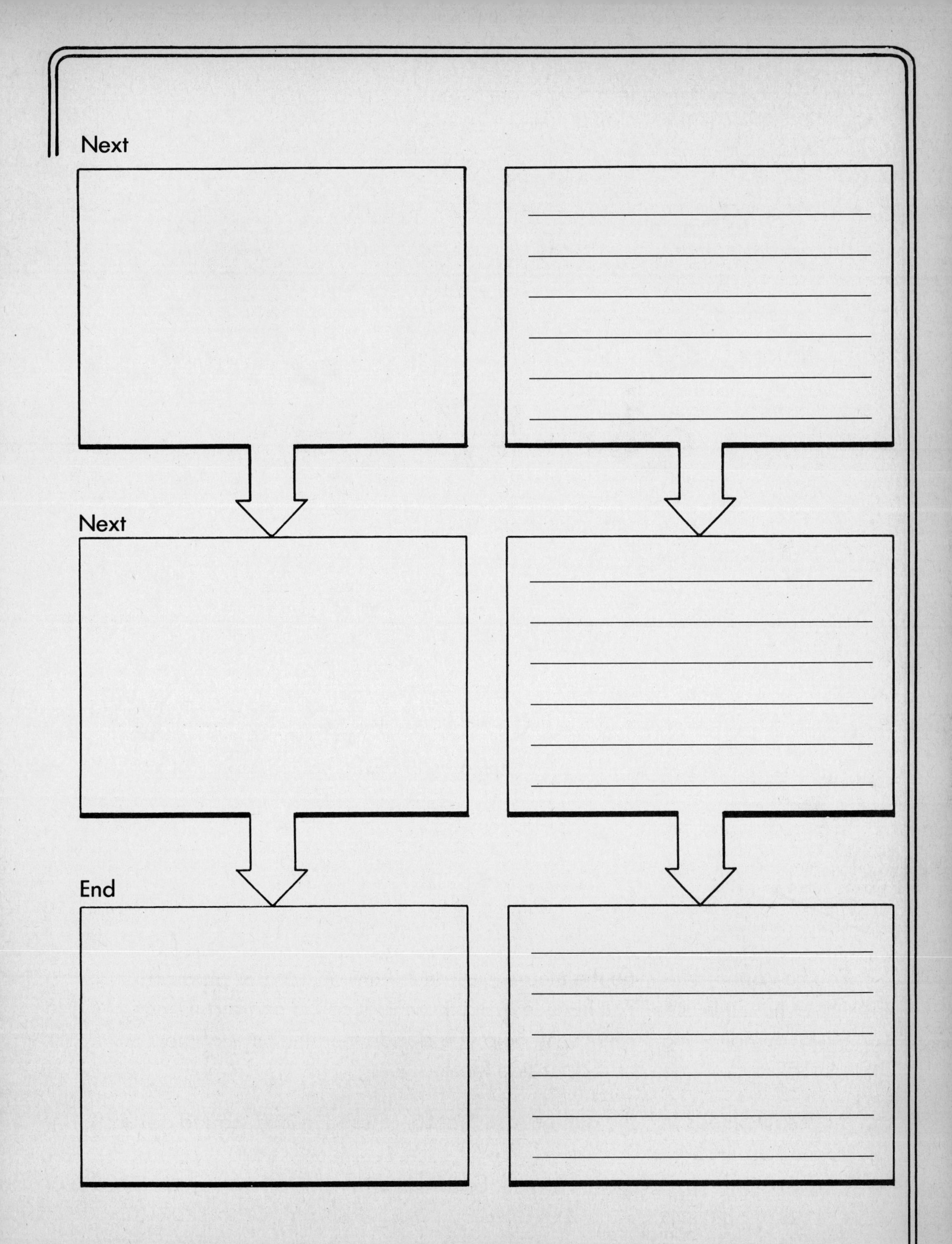
Next
Next
End

Use your map to retell "Mom Sleeps In" to a partner. If you left out important events, correct your map.

STEP BACK AND THINK **Vocabulary Development**

You can often determine the meaning of an unfamiliar word or phrase by looking at how it is used. You have learned that this is called **context.** Use the context of the following sentences to help you decide the meanings of the underlined words. Place a check beside the answers.

1. In "Mom Sleeps In," the author says that Laura used <u>intimidation</u> to get Josh to mop up the water.

   ________ honesty

   ________ humor

   ________ force

2. Dad suggested that it was time to negotiate some end of strike terms with Mom.

_________ discuss

_________ repair

_________ forget

3. The kids all answered in unison when Dad suggested they end the strike.

_________ by singing a song

_________ in a sad way

_________ at the same time

4. Several words used in "Mom Sleeps In" have more than one meaning. Read the following words from the story.

strike	sign	snap
alarm	handle	desert

Choose two of the words listed above. On the lines that follow, write two sentences with each word. Use the words in a different way in each sentence.

1st word: a. ______________________________

b. ______________________________

2nd word: c. ______________________________

d. ______________________________

STEP OUT ON YOUR OWN — Writing

"Mom Sleeps In" is a story about what might happen if mothers went on strike. Think about a person in your life who is very important to you—someone who takes care of you or helps you a lot. How would it affect you if this person suddenly went on strike? Write a story about what might happen. Use the space that follows to make some notes before you begin. ______________________

____

____

____

____

____

Choose the ideas you like best to use in your story. Begin your rough draft on the following lines. Use another piece of paper if you need more room. Be sure to give your story a title.

____

____

____

____

____

____

____

____

____

____

Read your rough draft carefully. Does it make sense? Did you leave out any important details? Does it have a good beginning and a good ending? Share it with some partners. Get their ideas; then revise your story to make it even better.

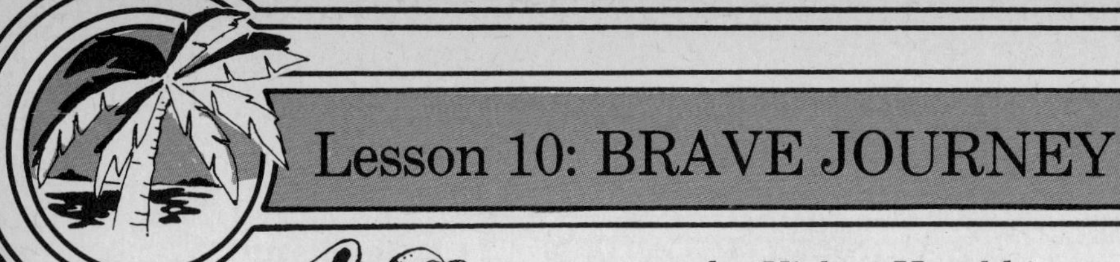

Lesson 10: BRAVE JOURNEY

by Vickey Herold

GET INTO STEP **Prior Knowledge**

1. Read each of the following questions very carefully. Answer at least one question on the lines below.

- Have you ever been in a dangerous situation?
- What would you do if your best friend were in trouble? Would you risk yourself for his or her safety?
- Think about a time when the weather caused you to feel very frightened. What happened?

___

___

___

___

2. What do you think "Brave Journey" will be about? Make some predictions.

___

___

___

___

STEP INTO THE STORY **Guided Reading**

Read "Brave Journey" to find out if any of your predictions are true. As you read, think about what you would do in a similar situation.

"The hurricane that has been forming in the Atlantic is heading inland. It should strike the Florida Keys within a matter of hours," the weatherman announced.

Lucy looked worried. "If only Dad were here," she thought. "If only he could get back from his business trip before the storm hits."

Lucy's mother must have known that Lucy was frightened. She tried to comfort her and Annie, Lucy's baby sister.

"We'll be all right, girls," Mother said in a soothing voice. "This is a good, strong house and we've been through these storms before. We've lived on the Keys for a long time, and we know what to do."

Has someone ever tried to calm your fears like Lucy's mother? ______________

If so, how did you feel about that person at the time? ______________

____

____

Lucy went to the door and looked outside. Everything seemed so deserted. The tourists had left the day before to get out ahead of the storm. Only the year–round residents remained, and there were very few of them. Those who lived closest to the shore had gone to the church that stood in the center of the island. Here, they would be safe inside the heavy, stone building. There was food there and cots to rest on. The church was always used as a shelter during hurricanes.

Lucy turned back to where her mother was sitting with Annie. Just then, the phone rang. It was Dad. He had called to say that he was worried because he couldn't get back home before the storm hit.

"We'll be fine," Mom answered firmly. "The Hawkins boys put up our storm shutters this morning and their dad brought us out some more batteries and an extra lantern. There's plenty of canned juice and food. Don't worry about us, Russell. We know how to ride out a hurricane."

Lucy was glad that her Mom was so confident. Listening to her talk to Dad made Lucy feel more confident, too.

Do you think that Lucy's mother is making a wise choice?____________

Would you stay or go to the church?____________

Why?____________

____

The weather broadcasts were coming more frequently now. The hurricane was moving with more speed than had been originally predicted. Unless a miracle happened, it would hit the island with its full force.

Suddenly, Lucy remembered her new friend, Mary Ann.

"What about Mary Ann's family, Mom?" Lucy cried. "They've never been through a hurricane before! They won't know what to do!"

"Oh, Lucy," Mom answered. "Surely they went to the church. They wouldn't stay in their little trailer house in a storm like this."

Mary Ann Watson, her younger brother and mom and dad had lived on the island for only a couple of months. Their little trailer home was parked in a lonely spot about a half mile from Lucy's house. Lucy knew that their trailer could never stand the fury of a hurricane. The storm could tear it to pieces.

"Mom!" she pleaded. "Somebody's got to warn them. This storm could kill them in that little trailer! Please let me go help them!"

What do you think Lucy's mother will say? Make a prediction.____________________

____

____

____

____

Mom knew that Lucy was right. If the Watsons didn't get to a shelter that could withstand the storm, they would be in grave danger.

"But Lucy," Mom answered. "I'm afraid for you to go. There may not be time for you to get back before the storm."

"I'll go to the church with the Watsons," Lucy pleaded. "I can stay there until it's passed."

Mom hesitated. She had to think.

"I won't stop you from going. But you must leave here at once and go as fast as you can. You must reach a safe place before the storm breaks. Head for the church and stay there until you're sure it's safe to come home."

Lucy nodded solemnly. She knew that she had a dangerous job ahead of her.

What do you think Lucy is feeling now? How would *you* feel if this were happening to you? Write some words to describe those feelings.

______________________ ______________________

______________________ ______________________

The storm had grown much worse than Lucy or her mother had realized. Lucy was truly frightened. As she fought to keep her balance in the forceful winds, she could hardly see where she was going. At last, she could see the trailer's outline through the rain. There was a light inside. They were still there.

"Mary Ann! Mary Ann!" Lucy shouted as she beat on the door of the trailer. Mr. Watson looked startled to see Lucy when he opened the door. He reached down and pulled her inside.

"What in the world are you doing out in this weather?" he asked.

"You can't stay here," she finally said. "You've got to get to the church. There's a hurricane headed right for us!"

Will Lucy convince the Watsons to leave their trailer? Make a prediction.

____

Just then a huge crash sounded and the whole trailer shook as something hit the back of it.

"It's a tree!" Mary Ann shouted as she ran in from the back of the trailer. "The whole thing is lying on the ground with its roots in the air! A big branch just hit the trailer when it fell!"

"You see!" Lucy said. "It's dangerous to stay here! We must get to church at once!"

The Watsons quickly pulled on rain coats and hats and started out into the night.

"Let's hold hands," shouted Lucy. "We have to make sure that we all stay together."

Each person clasped the other's hand tightly as they struggled against the wind and rain. It was so dark. There were no lights to be seen anywhere.

"The electric wires must be down," Mr. Watson shouted. "Watch out for live wires. Look where you step!"

Do you think Lucy and the Watsons will make it to the church? Will anyone be hurt or lost? Make a prediction.______________________________

____

____

Keep reading to find out if you're right.

As the group made its way through the storm, objects flew all about them—tree limbs, seaweed, shingles from roofs, pieces of tin and rock. Another tree crashed and fell with a thud behind them. Lucy swallowed hard as she realized how easily they could have been under the tree if it had fallen just seconds before.

Each of the victims struggled to take every step. The rain beat them relentlessly and stung their face and hands like tiny bullets. Their journey seemed endless.

"There!" shouted Mary Ann as she pointed between some trees. "Look there! There's a light ahead. It must be the church!"

"Yes!" agreed Mr. Watson. "I think it is!" He led the line of weary travelers toward the lantern light that spilled out from around the storm shutters.

Once inside the church, Lucy and the Watsons collapsed in total fatigue as their friends and neighbors rushed to help them with blankets and warm tea.

As Lucy huddled in her blanket, she was experiencing a strange mixture of feelings—both relief and uneasiness. She knew that she was safe, but what about her mother and little sister? Was their house holding up through the storm? Were they safe? Lucy couldn't rest for the remaining time that the hurricane raged. Her thoughts were with her family.

When the storm began to die down, Lucy announced that she was heading for home. "I have to make sure my mom and sister are all right."

"I'm going with you," said Mr. Watson.

"You don't have to do that," Lucy answered. "You should stay with your family."

"You stuck your neck out for us when we needed help," Mr. Watson stated firmly. "And I'm going to do the same for you."

Why do you think Mr. Watson is insisting on going with Lucy? ______________

____

What do you think they will find? ______________________________

____

The two of them started back toward Lucy's house. The storm was calming down quickly and they were able to move fast. Only once did they stop. The sight of the Watsons' trailer lying on its side crushed by a huge tree across its middle made Lucy and Mr. Watson stop and stare in horror.

At last Lucy saw her house through the trees. It was still standing! Lucy began running toward it with all the speed she could manage. Mother must have been watching for her because she met Lucy halfway there. The two hugged and cried and talked all at once to tell how happy each was to find the other safe.

Mr. Watson told Lucy's mom all about what had happened and about how thankful he was for Lucy's help.

"She saved our lives," he told Mom. "We can always get another trailer. We're just so glad that our family is safe."

"So are we, Mr. Watson," Mother agreed. "So are we!"

There are no right or wrong answers to the next questions. Think about them carefully, however, and write answers that make sense.

- This story never explains why Lucy's mother agreed to let Lucy go warn the Watsons. Why do you think Lucy's mother let her go? ____________________

____

____

- Several important **morals,** or lessons, could be learned from this story. Write a lesson that you think is important. ____________________

____

____

Share your answers with a partner who has also read "Brave Journey." Discuss why your answers are alike and why they are different.

Story Mapping

Have you figured out the main events in "Brave Journey"? In the boxes on the left, make a drawing or write key words to help you remember the order of the events in the story. Think about these events and write a story map in the shapes that are provided. Remember, you may not always need to use all the spaces. Be sure to include information about the setting.

THE SETTING

Main Characters:

Place:

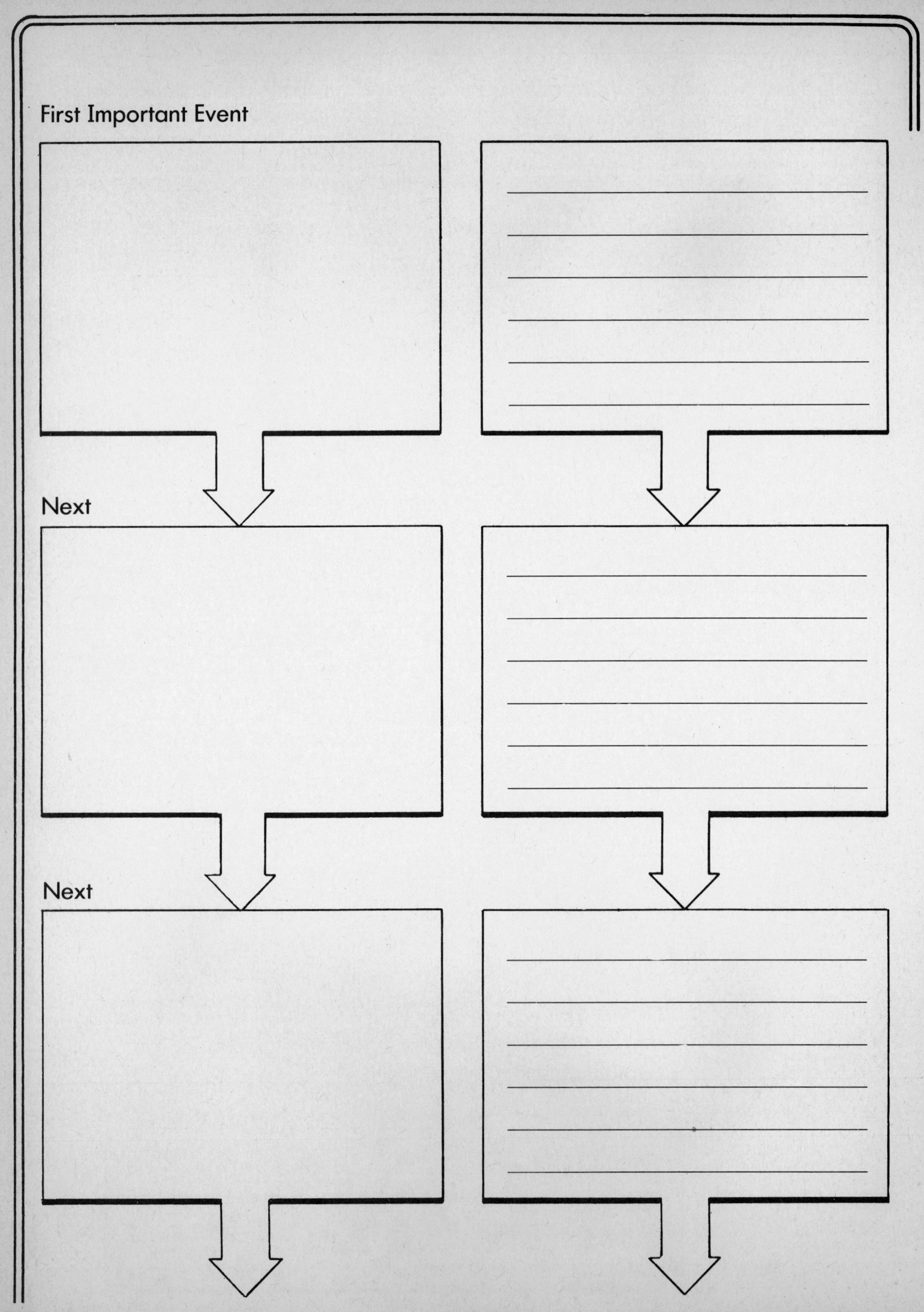

First Important Event
Next
Next

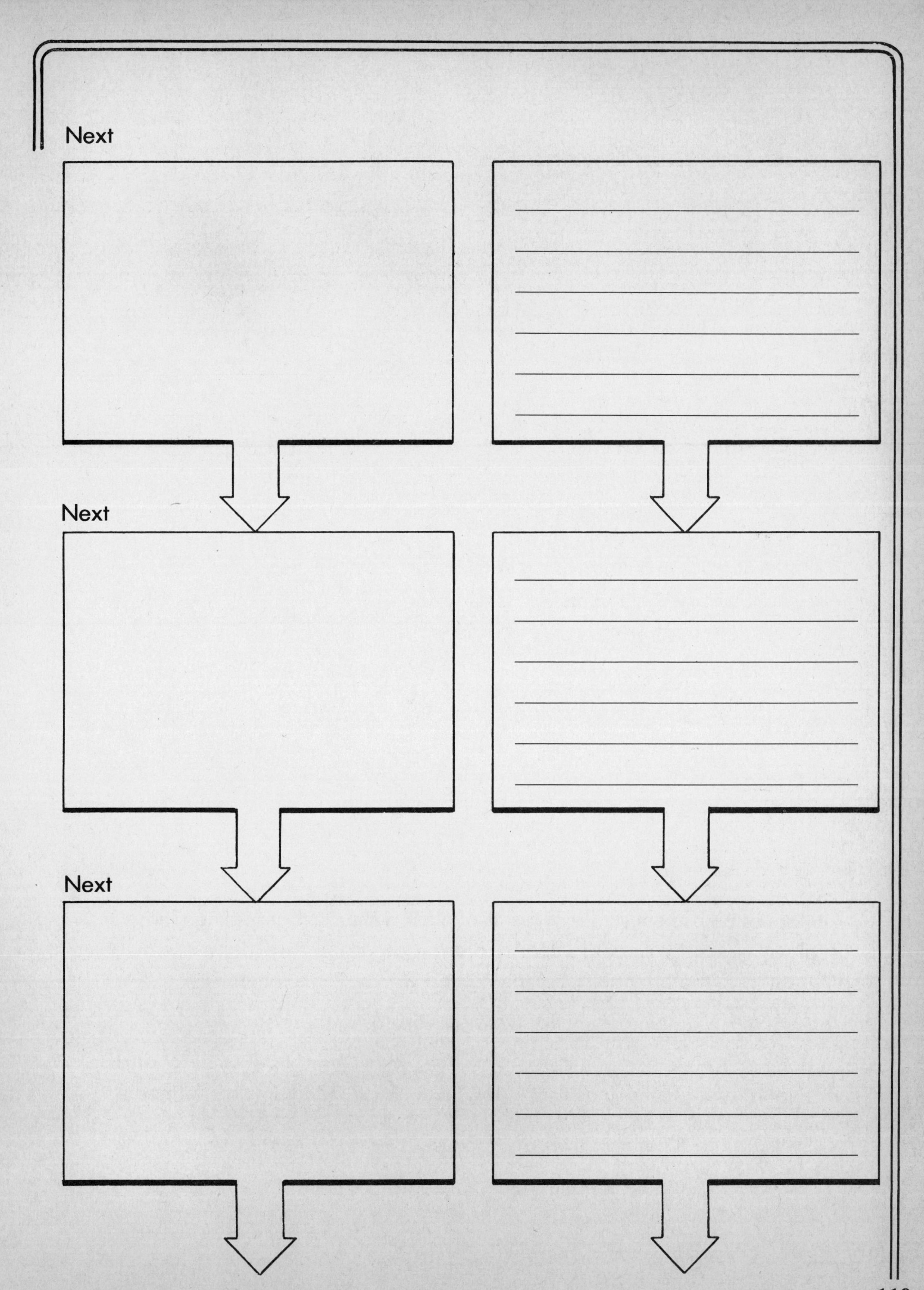

Next
Next
Next

Share your map with a partner who also mapped the story. How are your maps alike? How are they different? Use them to retell "Brave Journey." Did the maps help you and your partner retell the important events in the story? If so, both maps are correct, even if they are different.

STEP BACK AND THINK **Vocabulary Development**

Authors often use unusual sayings to explain a situation or feeling. These unusual sayings are called **idioms.** An **idiom** is a group of words whose meaning is different from the ordinary meanings of the words. For example:

Juan is *in hot water* for breaking the dish.

What does *in hot water* mean in this sentence? Read the following idioms from "Brave Journey." On the lines that follow, write what the idioms really mean.

1. Lucy's mom told her not to worry because they knew how to *ride out a hurricane.* What did she mean? ______________________________

____

____

2. Mr. Watson insisted on going back with Lucy after the storm. He said that she had *stuck her neck out* for them and that he would do the same for her.

   What did he mean? ______________________________

   ____

   ____

3. The following list contains several idioms that are not in "Brave Journey." However, you may have heard them used before. Choose at least one idiom to use in a sentence about something that has happened to you. Write the sentence on the lines that follow.

   - keep my chin up
   - face the music
   - see eye to eye
   - by the skin of my teeth

   ____

   ____

In "Brave Journey" the author uses many descriptive words to help her readers understand the fury of the hurricane. Read each of the following situations. On the lines that follow, write the most descriptive words you can think of to describe each situation.

4. What words could you use to describe a wrecked car?

______________________ ______________________

______________________ ______________________

5. What words could you use to describe how a new puppy makes you feel?

______________________ ______________________

______________________ ______________________

6. What words could best describe the sounds of a video game arcade?

______________________ ______________________

______________________ ______________________

7. What words could you use to describe the way your favorite dinner smells?

______________________ ______________________

______________________ ______________________

STEP OUT ON YOUR OWN **Writing**

"Brave Journey" describes a very brave and dangerous event. Think of an event in your life that was special. It may be something frightening like what happened to Lucy, or it may be something funny, exciting or sad. Describe the event in a story that helps your readers really understand what happened and how you felt. Think of some powerful words that can bring your story to life for your audience. Use the following lines to make some notes before you begin your first draft. ______

Choose the ideas you think are best and write your story. You may begin your rough draft on the lines that follow. Use another piece of paper to finish. Be sure to give your story a title.

Share your story with a partner or with your teacher. Ask them for suggestions that will make your writing even better. Use their ideas when you revise.

ANSWER KEY

Lesson 1—INCIDENT AT DICKENS CREEK

Stay in Step

1. The story takes place at Dickens Creek.
2. The main characters are Donnie and his cousin, Ned.
3. Donnie thinks that Ned acts like a nerd and will embarrass him on the camp – out.
4. Ned coughs, sneezes, wheezes and complains about everything. He constantly uses nasal spray.
5. Donnie discovers a big bear outside the tent.
6. Ned helps Donnie scare the bear away by spraying nasal spray in the creature's face.
7. The boys decide to ask Ned to go on the next camp – out. They also plan to take several bottles of nasal spray.

Step Back and Think

1. Answers may vary but should indicate that a nerd is a person whose behavior is weird or strange—not like everyone else's.
2. Answers might include the following examples:
   Ned wears a red and black checked hat with ear flaps.
   Ned takes a suitcase and briefcase on the campout.
   Ned constantly coughs and wheezes.
   Ned wears silly looking glasses.
   Ned complains about the cold, the wind, the dampness and the smoke from the fire.
   Ned uses nasal spray constantly.
3. Answers may vary but should be similar to *brave, hero, quick-thinking,* and so on.
4. a. Answers may vary but should be similar to *bully.*
   b. Answers may vary but should be similar to *hero.*
   c. Answers may vary but should be similar to *crook, thief, sneak, robber.*
5. Answers may vary but should indicate that Ned was not a pleasant person to be around.
6. Answers may vary but should indicate that Donnie wasn't physically sick but extremely unhappy that Cousin Ned was coming to visit.

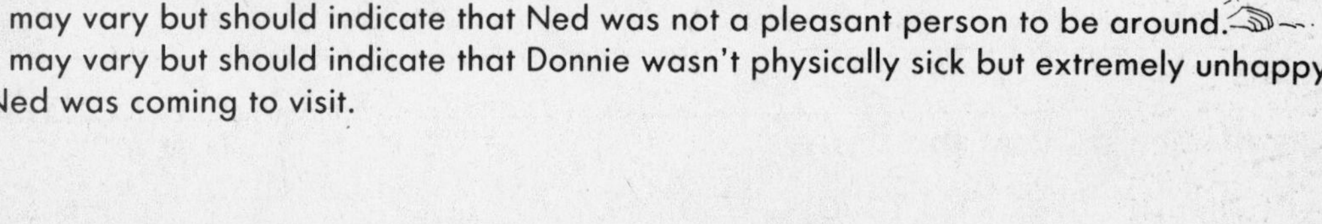

Lesson 2—THE LITTLE OLD LADY WHO LIKED SPIDERS

Stay in Step

1. The story takes place at Lolly's house.
2. The main characters are Lolly and Victoria.
3. Lolly's Christmas tree is small and sparsely decorated with old, worn–out ornaments.
4. The spiders want to give Lolly a gift because she has treated them so kindly.
5. Victoria suggests that the spiders spin elegant, silvery webs over the entire tree to surprise Lolly.
6. Lolly thanks her friends for the loveliest Christmas present she has ever had.
   Answers to the story map should include most of the above events.

Step Back and Think

1. sad
2. Answers may vary but should indicate that a person with regal bearing should act like a king or queen—stately, royal, proud.
3. Answers will vary.
4. Answers will vary.
5. Answers will vary.

6. Answers will vary.
7. Answers will vary.
8. Answers will vary.
9. Answers will vary.

Lesson 3—THE NEW HAMPSHIRE KIDNAPPING

Stay in Step

Story map answers should include most of the following events:

- Betty and Barney are hypnotized and begin telling about their strange experience.
- Betty and Barney are examined by the strange creatures.
- Betty and Barney are released unharmed.
- Betty and Barney's experience becomes known as one of the most famous UFO encounters in the world. The Hills become famous appearing on radio and television. A book is even written about their experience.

Step Back and Think

1. Answers may vary but should indicate that Barney was troubled about something.
2. Answers may vary.
3. unpleasant
4. pleasant
5. pleasant
6. unpleasant
7. Betsy
8. Tom
9. Mom

Lesson 4—THE PERFECT HIDING PLACE

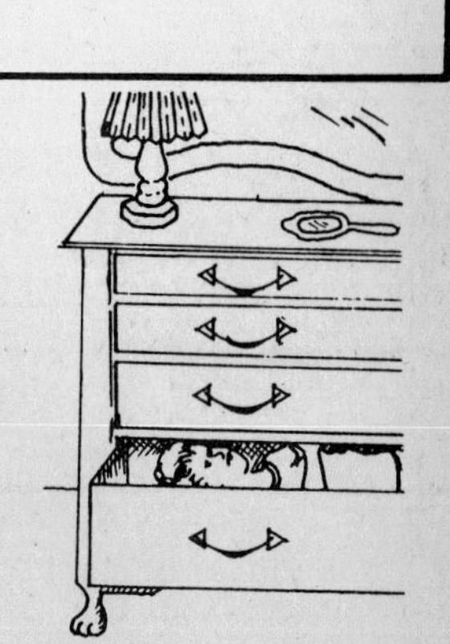

Stay in Step

Main Characters: Sheila, Larry

Place: an old, three-story house

Story map answers should include most of the following events:

- Sheila tries to find the perfect hiding place where her brother, Larry, cannot find her.
- She decides to hide in a dresser drawer.
- The drawer sticks, and Sheila is trapped until her mother rescues her.
- Larry suggests that they play hide-and-seek.
- Sheila, still unable to think of a good hiding place, crawls under the quilt on her bed.
- Larry searches the entire house, but he is unable to find Sheila because she has discovered the perfect hiding place.

Step Back and Think

1. The two things being compared are the old house and a person in pain. They are alike because they both make noises.
2. The two things being compared are the inside of a drawer and a damp forest full of toadstools, vultures and bats. They are alike because they both smell old, musty and creepy. Answers may vary but should indicate that the main character feels anxious, fearful or uneasy about her surroundings.
3. a. Answers will vary.
   b. Answers will vary.

c. Answers will vary.
d. Answers will vary.
e. Answers will vary.
f. Answers will vary.
g. Answers will vary.
h. Answers will vary.
4. Answers may vary but should indicate "self-satisfied; pleased with oneself."
5. Answers may vary.
6. Answers may vary but should include similar answers: sofa, divan, couch.

Lesson 5—DEAR AUNT HELEN

Stay in Step

Main Characters—Joseph, Aunt Helen
Place—Joseph's home and school
Story map answers should include most of these events:

- Joseph is unhappy when he is given the assignment to write to a lady in a retirement home.
- Joseph writes Mrs. Helen Smith. She writes him back and asks him to call her Aunt Helen.
- Joseph begins to write Aunt Helen more often, but doesn't tell anyone.
- Aunt Helen gives Joseph good advice on how to handle his grandfather's death and help his mother and grandmother.
- Joseph keeps writing Aunt Helen. He tells her that every guy needs one secret, and she is his.

Step Back and Think

1. Answers may vary but should indicate "walked in a tired way or with effort."
2. plodded
   shuffled
3. Answers may vary but should indicate "surprised greatly or amazed."
4. Answers may vary.
5. Joseph's arm was tired and hurting.

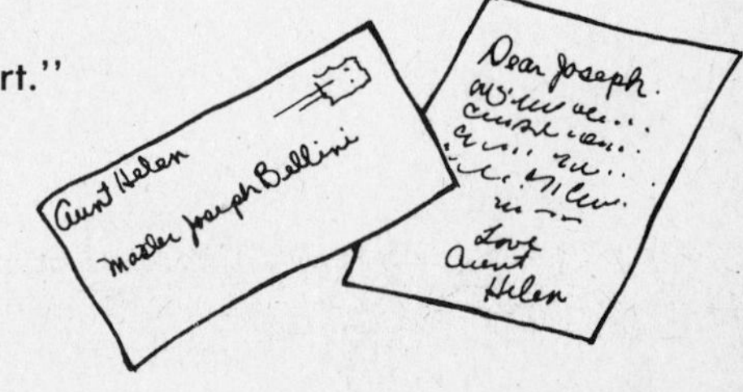

Lesson 6—REMEMBERING LAST SUMMER (PART I)

Stay in Step

Main Characters: Bobby Nelson, Grandma, Pepper, and the narrator
Place: one summer in a small town
Story map should include most of the following events:

- Bobby Nelson, the narrator's best friend, moves to Ohio.
- The narrator takes her dog, Pepper, everywhere after Bobby moves.
- Pepper suddenly dies and is buried in the back yard.
- The narrator is heartbroken.

Step Back and Think

1. Answers will vary but may include *sad, unhappy, numb* and so on.
2. Answers will vary.
3. Answers will vary.
4. Pepper sang as loudly and happily as he could.
5. Answers will vary.

Lesson 7—REMEMBERING LAST SUMMER (PART II)

Stay in Step

Main Characters: Grandmother and the narrator
Place: a small town
Story map answers should include most of these events:

- Grandmother tries to comfort the narrator the morning after Pepper dies.
- Grandmother and the narrator plant a small tree over Pepper's grave.
- The tree, a dogwood, blooms the following spring.
- The narrator discovers that her grandmother may be her very best friend of all.

Step Back and Think

1. Answers will vary.
2. Answers will vary.
3. Answers will vary.
4. Answers will vary.
5. Answers will vary.
6. Answers will vary.
7. a. Answers will vary but should indicate a similar grouping:
   Happy
   cheerful
   laughing
   twinkle
   beaming
   surprise
   b. Answers will vary but should indicate a similar grouping:
   Sad
   quiet
   dreary
   cry
   angry
   miserable
   dark
   c. Answers will vary.

Lesson 8—THE HORRIBLE HUDSONS

Stay in Step

Main Characters: Jenny, Justin, Jason
Place: The Hudson house
Story map answers should include most of the following events:

- Jenny is babysitting for the Hudson twins.
- Jason and Justin tell Jenny that they intend to do whatever they want, no matter what she says.
- The twins use the furniture like a trampoline. They scare the cat and break a lamp.
- Jenny insists that the twins go to bed.
- Instead of reading "baby" stories to the boys, Jenny tells them stories from a book she is reading.
- The twins enjoy the stories, and they finally fall asleep.

Step Back and Think

1. unpleasant
2. pleasant
3. pleasant

4. unpleasant
5. pleasant
6. unpleasant
7. The two things being compared are the twins and monsters.
   They are alike because they both torment people.
8. The two things being compared are the twins and soldiers.
   They are alike because the twins were jumping from the furniture the way soldiers parachute from airplanes.

Lesson 9—MOM SLEEPS IN

Stay in Step

Main Characters: Laura, Sarah, Josh, Mother, Dad

Place: Laura's house

Story map answers should include most of these events:

- Laura's clock radio awakens her with a newsflash announcing that "all mothers are on strike today."
- When Laura's mother doesn't wake her at 7:00 a.m., Laura finds her still sleeping.
- Laura discovers Josh dressed all wrong and water from the bathroom sink flooding his room.
- Dad gets out of the shower, sees the mess and decides to get Mom.
- Mother agrees to end the strike.
- The entire family helps clean up the mess.

Step Back and Think

1. force
2. discuss
3. at the same time
4. a. Answers will vary.
   b. Answers will vary.
   c. Answers will vary.
   d. Answers will vary.

Lesson 10—BRAVE JOURNEY

Stay in Step

Main Characters: Lucy, Mr. Watson, Mother

Place: Florida Keys

Story map answers should include most of these events:

- A hurricane is headed for the Florida Keys. Lucy's father is unable to return home before the storm hits.
- Lucy leaves her home to warn the Watson family about the danger of staying in their trailer during the storm.
- Lucy and the Watsons reach the safety of the church.
- As soon as the storm begins to die down, Lucy returns home to see if her family is safe. Mr. Watson insists on going with her.
- Lucy and Mr. Watson see that their trailer has been demolished by the storm. They realize what would have happened if Lucy hadn't warned the Watsons.
- Lucy finds her house undamaged, and her family safe.

Step Back and Think

1. Lucy's mother means that they know how to remain safe during the dangerous storm.
2. Mr. Watson means that Lucy had helped his family and now it was time to help her.
3. Answers will vary.
4. Answers will vary.
5. Answers will vary.
6. Answers will vary.
7. Answers will vary.